My
Best Friends
ON THE TITANIC

Sally
Morgan

Illustrated by
Gareth
Conway

To my darling Lily and Daisy.
Let's make fairings!

Scholastic Children's Books,
Euston House, 24 Eversholt Street,
London NW1 1DB, UK

A division of Scholastic Ltd
London ~ New York ~ Toronto ~ Sydney ~ Auckland
Mexico City ~ New Delhi ~ Hong Kong

Published in the UK by Scholastic Ltd, 2019

ISBN 978 1407 19455 4

Printed and bound in the UK by CPI Group (UK) Ltd, Croydon, CR0 4YY

2 4 6 8 10 9 7 5 3 1

The right of Sally Morgan and Gareth Conway to be identified as the author and
illustr... ...ccordance with the

The Baxters

Mr Baxter

Ginny

Mrs Baxter

Dorothy (Dot)

Tom

The Taylors

William (Dash)

Mr Taylor

Dear Reader,

You have in your hands some incredibly rare and important messages. These **LETTERS**, **MARCONIGRAMS**[1] and **MISSION REPORTS** have travelled thousands of miles, crossed oceans and have even survived pesky parents and little sisters as well as ~~unsinkable~~ unthinkable tragedy.

Dorothy and I began writing in 1911 when our parents made the decision to move our families from Cornwall in the United Kingdom to America. Our fathers had been friends for a long time and dreamed of starting an apple farm in upstate New York. When they found just the right place, the plan was for our dads and me to sail over there first and get the house and farm ready. Dorothy and her mother, brother and baby sister, Ginny, were to sail out later when they had sold the house in Cornwall. Dorothy was **NOT PLEASED** to be left behind.

Dorothy and I had to find lots of inventive ways of keeping in touch while we went on our separate adventures. We knew it was an exciting time but we had no idea about the terrifying events that were about to unfold.

Everybody knows the story of Titanic – the magnificent ship that set sail from Southampton to New York on its maiden voyage only to strike an iceberg and sink down into the icy depths of the Atlantic Ocean. But they don't know the story quite like my best friend Dorothy and I do.

I hope you enjoy reading our messages.

Love,

William (Dash) Taylor

---

1 A message sent by wireless telegraphy.

Dear Dotty,

We made it to Belfast! It took a while but we are here, staying with my grandparents. They are spoiling me **ROTTEN.** I see why you like living so close to yours. You will miss them when we move to America, I'm sure.

Dad hadn't told them we were moving to America, and he finally spilled the beans **LAST NIGHT!** I thought they'd be sad, but they said that they always knew Dad was **GOING PLACES** and that we would have a **GRAND TIME** together. They said they hoped it would be a new start for us both after losing Mam to consumption[2] last year. I wasn't so sure about that. I know for a fact I'll always miss her, no matter where I live.

Dad's brother, Uncle Michael, and my cousin Ronald came over, too. Uncle Michael wasn't surprised we were going either. He said Dad always had **BIG IDEAS.** He didn't mind Dad making his fortune in America as long as he sent him some back, as he'd taught Dad **EVERYTHING HE KNOWS.** Dad laughed and said that seemed fair, seeing as Uncle Michael had put up with him being so **CHEEKY** when they were growing up. They pretended to have a fight.

I haven't seen Dad laugh so much since Mam died. It was strange, but it felt good to see him happy.

I wasn't sure if I was going to like letter-writing after you suggested it. It is a bit slow but there is **ONE GOOD THING** about it. I can call you

2 Consumption is another name for tuberculosis, a disease that mostly affects the lungs and killed many people until the introduction of a vaccine in the 1920s. Now tuberculosis can be treated with antibiotics that were not available in William and Dorothy's time.

'Dotty' and there is nothing you can do about it. Ha! If you want to get cross or call me a name in return, it will take days for you to tell me so. Isn't that **BRILLIANT**? It will take even longer for you to get annoyed with me when I'm in America and you're in Cornwall.

I wish you and your brother, Tom, were sailing with us when we go. It would be much more fun with you along for the ride. Perhaps I should try to be as **ANNOYING AS POSSIBLE** in my letters so that you won't miss me.

I wish you had been here today, too. You'd have loved it! Uncle Michael got us tickets to see the launch of the colossal passenger liner, RMS Titanic, from the Harland and Wolff shipyard. **WHAT A SHIP!** I say ship, but it looked more like a **FLOATING CITY** really! It towered over our heads, its four funnels **PUSHING INTO THE SKY**. I counted 10 decks but Uncle Michael said there were 11. The bottom of the ship is painted red. That's the bit that is below the waterline and so most people wouldn't really get to see it. The funnels are black with a beigey yellow stripe that made them look very smart. Uncle Michael said the colour is an extra special colour made for the White Star Line called White Star Buff.

It looked like it must be nearly a mile long. Uncle Michael said it was 882 feet (269 metres), which was a **LONG WAY OFF** being a mile, but was still longer than any other ship ever built except its sister, RMS Olympic. He's talked non-stop about how he will be working on it - he's a joiner[3] just like Dad. White Star Line are hiring the best in the business to make RMS Olympic and Titanic the **BIGGEST AND MOST LUXURIOUS** ships to ever sail.

3 A joiner is a type of carpenter.

Dad said it was always a **BIG DEAL** when a ship is launched, but that Titanic was **SOMETHING SPECIAL**. He had never seen so many people line the dock.[4]

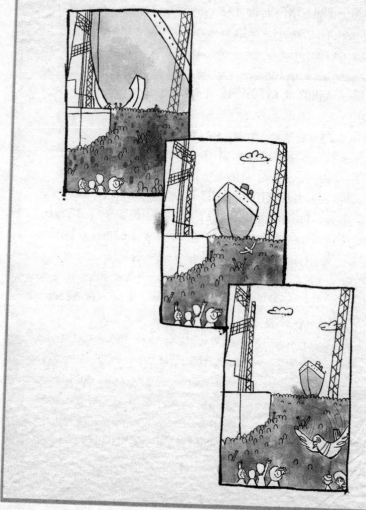

4 100,000 people watched the launch.

At noon a **ROCKET WAS FIRED** to announce the ship was about to launch. Fifteen minutes later there was another **BOOM**, and off it went. Despite its **ENORMOUS** size, **THE GREAT SHIP** can't have taken much more than a minute to **SLIDE** down the slipway.[5] It was amazing to see something so big enter the water. Like a **GIANT DUCK** plopping into a pond. Uncle Michael said that they had to grease the slipway with tallow and soap to get it to move, just like when you are trying to get a ring off that has got stuck on your finger. They must have used **TONS** to stop it from getting stuck.[6]

Once it was in the water it was pulled deeper by tug boats that looked tiny in comparison - and off it went.

Is that it?

If watching the launch of the largest ship ever to set sail doesn't impress you, I don't know what will!

5 It took 62 seconds!
6 Tallow is a kind of animal fat, and they really did use 22 tons of it to launch RMS *Titanic*. The slipway was covered with over an inch of tallow, soap and oil from the fat of sperm whales. Yuck!

I'd heard that to launch a ship, a lady in a **BIG FLOUNCY HAT** has to smash a bottle of champagne against it for good luck[7], but that's not what happened at all. It just slid into the water. I asked Uncle Michael if that meant Titanic would have bad luck. He said it was a **GOOD THING** too, because if the lady in the **BIG FLOUNCY HAT** didn't swing the bottle hard enough and it **DIDN'T SMASH**, it could mean **VERY BAD LUCK**.[8]

Wait! Wait! It didn't smash!

A girl standing nearby said Titanic was worse than unlucky - it was **HAUNTED**. She said one of the shipyard workers had got trapped in the hull. She'd heard that if you went wandering around the shipyard at night you could hear him **TAPPING** and **BEGGING** to be let out. **YIKES!** Uncle Michael burst out **LAUGHING** and told her there was no one trapped in the hull. He and his pals had made up that story to scare some of the new boys into being careful. But he told us that **EIGHT MEN HAD DIED** building the Titanic, some from falls, others by being **CRUSHED TO DEATH** by enormous bits of timber and metal used to build a ship that size. I can believe it too. I heard the anchor was so large that it took many horses to shift it! Uncle Michael said building ships is dangerous work. **MORE THAN 3,000 MEN** had worked on Titanic,

7 Often when new ships are launched they are given a good luck ceremony which involves an important person smashing a bottle of champagne over their bow (pointy front end) to wish them well.

8 Some people believe the fact *Titanic* was not given such a ceremony may have caused the sinking. This is a myth because the White Star Line never launched their new ships in that way.

and although people were careful, accidents were bound to happen.

I can't imagine what it would feel like to have worked on something like that.

"We just build them and shove 'em in," Uncle Michael said, waving at the water.

But you could tell he was proud.

I wished we could take a look inside, but Uncle Michael said it wasn't much to look at yet. If Olympic is anything to go by though, it's going to be an amazing sight! He showed me a leaflet and it looked fancier than anywhere I've ever been! A bit like a jewellery box. Intricately carved woodwork, gleaming brass and real marble too! I can't imagine what it would cost! I think it would be like **TRAVELLING IN A PALACE**.

When we got back, I asked Dad if he wished he could work on something like that. He said he'd leave the ship-building to his brother. He was the type of person who preferred to sail on them in comfort. Uncle Michael **KNOCKED HIS CAP OFF** and said he could see Dad fitting in well in America as the country was just big enough to fit his **ENORMOUS HEAD**, because his hat clearly wasn't. Dad chased him up the street as if they were boys. It made me miss you and Tom.

I hope I make some good friends in America, though I am sure I won't meet anyone as fun as you. You'll just have to hurry up and join me, then the **REAL ADVENTURES** can begin.

From,

William

Dear Will,

I'm glad you are both having a lovely time. It must be nice seeing your dad so happy, it's nice to hear you sound happy too. America will be a **NEW START** for all of us, but I know you will always miss your mother. I miss her too. I can't imagine what it would be like to lose mine. She can drive me crazy but, whenever I think about it, I feel terrible about all of the times I've been naughty or said unkind things about her cooking.

Titanic sounds **MAGNIFICENT**. Your Uncle Michael should be proud. It's hard to picture something that size being able to float let alone sail all the way **ACROSS THE ATLANTIC**. You'd think it would be **IMPOSSIBLE**. It's mad to think we're both going to make that journey soon, even if our ships won't be as fancy as Titanic.

Tom wrestled your letter off me because he wanted to hear all about the ship. He was impressed. You know how much he likes facts - **BIGGESTS**, **TALLESTS**, **FASTESTS**, **FIRSTS**, anything like that. I'm sure he'll know far more than you about Titanic by the time you get back. He will be talking about the launch as though he had been there himself.

I'm glad you've warmed to writing letters. You are right! I don't like being called Dotty, and I don't like it any more in a letter than I do in person.

You are **SO ANNOYING** which is why I gave you a new name, too. I hope you like it.

Hello there! My name is Will-I-Am-Annoying!

I think it is a great way to introduce yourself to all the **NEW PEOPLE** you meet when you go to America. I am sure the Americans will appreciate such a helpful introduction. They will know what they are getting into before they commit to **ACTUALLY BEING FRIENDS** with you.

I'm glad you are having a good time in Belfast. We miss you here. Father has put the house up for sale and hopes to hear about a buyer any day now. I hope it's **SOON** so we can come with you after all. Though Mother says that's unlikely.

I'm glad to hear the ship wasn't really **HAUNTED**!

I'm nervous enough about sailing without imagining **GHOSTS** roaming the decks at night. I'll have to get used to the idea of sailing before we go. Especially if I want to **TRAVEL THE WORLD** when we grow up. Grandma has been helping me with my French and says I am getting as good as her. It's hard to know without any real French people to speak to.

Speaking of ghosts, Grandad said he is going to tell everyone that **OUR HOUSE IS HAUNTED** because he doesn't want us to leave!

I'm not sure I want to leave either. I will be so sad to say goodbye to everyone, even if I am excited about my first **BIG ADVENTURE**. I'm so annoyed you will be doing it before me!

Yours truly,

Dorothy

Dear Dotty,

Your new name for me is **VERY FUNNY**! I laughed so hard when I read it. But **THEN**, I realized something that will **ANNOY YOU**. My name offers almost endless possibilities. I **WILL** admit, I **AM** annoying, but I **AM** also **BRILLIANT**, **AMAZING** and **DEVILISHLY HANDSOME** and so I can choose any of these nicknames when introducing myself.

Are you sick of **LETTER-WRITING** yet? Never fear, I've discovered a **BRAND-NEW COMMUNICATION METHOD** that is going to change everything. Well, I didn't discover it, a man called Guglielmo Marconi did.[9]

You know how you were worried we wouldn't be able to tell each other our news when I got to America? Well we will! With **RADIOTELEGRAPHY**! We can send each other messages, in code, across the Atlantic. All thanks

9 Italian inventor Guglielmo Marconi developed the most successful radio telegraph device able to transmit and receive messages over long distances. He transmitted the first trans-Atlantic message in 1901.

to Guglielmo Marconi and my cousin Ronald, the one who worked at the post office as a telegraph operator.

Ronald goes to the **MARCONI SCHOOL** near Liverpool and is training to become a Marconi operator and work on ships, just like Titanic. He showed me the brochure, he said he would get to wear a **FANCY UNIFORM** and sail around the world sending very important messages. It sounds a lot more fun than sitting in the village post office tapping out notes about horribly sick aunts and delayed deliveries of potatoes like he used to do.

Before wireless telegraphy, ships had to communicate with all these different flags which meant they had to be in sight of one another.[10]

Radiotelegraphy is a lot like sending a normal telegram. When you send a telegram, you write a message on a slip of paper and then an operator (like Ronald when he worked at the post office) turns your message into a series of dots and dashes and taps these out using a telegraph key. They press the key quickly for a dot and hold it down a little longer for a dash. These dots and dashes are called Morse code. Pressing down the key sends an electrical pulse **WHIZZING** down a wire to the receiver who listens to the dots and dashes that sound like beeps. **BUP, BUP, BUP, BUP, BEEP, BEEP.** The receiver decodes all these beeps into the original message which they write down on a slip of paper and get someone to deliver to the recipient's house. Easy peasy.

The telegraph is **BRILLIANT** and there doesn't seem to be a limit to how long the wires are, stretching the whole length of countries and passing **UNDER OCEANS**.

---

10 International maritime signal flags were used to help ships to communicate important information to one another. Flags could be used to spell out messages in code or individual flags could be used to warn other ships of danger or ask for help.

These wires are how you can read about what happened yesterday in Egypt or India or America.

You see? **BRILLIANT.** But sending telegrams to and from America is very expensive and it would take a long time to walk to the post office to send a message every time I wanted to tell you something. It would be quicker than writing letters, but still. Also, if the wires break, which happens, you are left having to post the same letter again. **NOT BRILLIANT.**[11]

---

11 Before the telegraph cable, communication between Europe and North America was by ship. The first Atlantic cable was completed in 1858. It was very expensive and broke not long after it was laid. A better cable was laid in 1866 and was followed by many more.

Imagine if you could send messages by tapping them out yourself, without wires. That's what radiotelegraphy is. With wireless telegraphy, when the message is tapped, instead of sending electrical pulses down a wire, it sends out **ELECTROMAGNETIC WAVES** called radio waves. These waves **FLY THROUGH THE AIR** until they are picked up by a receiver and translated back into words, just like with a normal telegraph. Unlike miles upon miles of expensive wire, air doesn't cost a thing. Nobody owns it and so anyone can send radio waves through it. Well, anyone who has all the gear and understands Morse code.

Marconi has already sent the first message from England to Newfoundland. Isn't that amazing? Better still, he sent it from **CORNWALL**, just down the road in Poldhu.[12]

I didn't know how easy it was to build your own transmitter and receiver, either. I couldn't believe it when Ronald showed me his set-up. Your grandad is going to love it. I know how he likes tinkering. You will like it too, because you have to learn a **NEW LANGUAGE** in order to use it. Well not a new language exactly, but you have to relearn the alphabet in Morse code. Ronald had an extra copy so I popped it in the envelope with the letter. I've copied out one for myself. What do you think? Shall we try it! I want you to be **FLUENT** by the time I get back to Cornwall.

12 In 1901, radio pioneer Guglielmo Marconi sent the first wireless radio transmission across the Atlantic from Poldhu, Cornwall to Newfoundland (which is now a Canadian province). A distance of over 2000 miles. The message was the Morse code signal for the letter 's'.

MORSE CODE ALPHABET

A • —			N — •	
B — • • •			O — — —	
C — • — •			P • — — •	
D — • •			Q — — • —	
E •			R • — •	
F • • — •			S • • •	
G — — •			T —	
H • • • •			U • • —	
I • •			V • • • —	
J • — — —			W • — —	
K — • —			X — • • —	
L • — • •			Y — • — —	
M — —			Z — — • •	

This is your name in Morse code:

D O R O T H Y
−·· −−− ·−· −−− − ···· −·−−

But I think you should be Dotty which would be:

D O T T Y
−·· −−− − − −·−−

Or even Dot! **DOT** could be your call sign. Every radio operator has one. It is how you tell who is sending the message. You can choose anything you like, but I think **DOT** is perfect.[13]

D O T
−·· −−− −

I want to go to a Marconi School and be a Marconi Operator when I grow up, just like Ronald. To qualify you need to be between twenty-one and twenty-five years old, and male (I know - it's totally unfair) and be able to send messages at a speed of no less than **TWENTY-FIVE WORDS PER MINUTE**. I asked Ronald what would happen if all the words you had to send were really long. But he said that twenty-five words per minute was an average, so that would be OK. Often telegraph operators have to send messages **ALL DAY** or **ALL NIGHT**, depending on what shift they are working. I think my finger would fall off!

13 This was true until 1912 when new rules were introduced and people were given a call sign rather than choose their own.

There are **SO MANY** things to learn, because not only do you have to be able to send and receive messages, you also have to get to know the equipment really well, so that you can fix it if something breaks.

I think this is how everyone will communicate one day. Imagine sending **MESSAGES FLYING THROUGH THE AIR** to whoever you want, whenever you want, from a box you can hold in your hand?

If I don't become a Marconi operator, I will be a great inventor like Marconi and invent such a box and **MAKE A FORTUNE** selling them to people all over the world. Ronald laughed and said I should patent the idea now if I want to make any money from it. Apparently a patent is something you have to apply for that proves that something was your idea first and gives you the right to be the only person to make and sell your idea. I suppose I might need to know how it works first. Thinking caps on, eh?

Do write soon!

William

Dear William,

I like the name Dot much more than Dotty. I told Grandad about radiotelegraphy, and he already knew **ALL ABOUT IT**! He used to work at the post office, too, biking telegrams to people years and years ago. He said that being able to send messages without wires is like **MAGIC** and that he also believes that is how everyone will communicate one day. Grandma said that was because he has never been much of a letter writer. Anyway, he said he would help me build **MY OWN SET**.

He knows a bit of Morse code, too, but he's a bit rusty. He agreed that wireless will change everything, but that we shouldn't hold out much hope that we will be able to send messages across the Atlantic. It's still a **VERY NEW** technology!

Thanks for the Morse code alphabet, I am learning it with Tom. It's **SO USEFUL**. We use it to talk to each other at the dinner table without Mother knowing what we are saying.

Of course, Grandad knows, but he won't give us away. I know Mother suspects something though because I **SPAT OUT** half of my stew last night when Tom tapped out that it tasted like mouldy frogspawn!

Well he said 'mouldy frogsprawn' but I can't expect his spelling to be any better in Morse code than it is in English. He likes **FACTS**, not spelling.

I was about to tap something back when Mother said, "Concentrate on not **CHOKING** rather than starting that terrible tapping again!"

I did as she said, but she couldn't stop us tapping at bedtime. My room is next door to Tom's and the walls are thin:

"Do you think we will still be able to hear dad snoring when he is in America?" I tapped.

I could hear him laughing through the wall.

"Go to sleep you pesky pair of woodpeckers." Grandad called from downstairs.

It will be lots more fun when we have our real radio all set up!

Very best wishes,

Dot

25th June 1911
Belfast

Dear Dot,

I **KNEW** your grandad would know all about radiotelegraphy. I bet you will already have a great set-up by the time I get back, and you will be quick at **MORSE CODE**, too. I think it's great that you and Tom are already practising. I never thought about using it to send secret messages to someone in the same room. **GENIUS!** Trust you and Tom to come up with that.

I'm determined to be a **MARCONI OPERATOR** now, though I think I may have started to annoy Ronald with all my questions. When he came to Grandma and Grandad's this morning he had a box of articles and clippings to keep me quiet.

I went through them all and, along with all the Marconi brochures and bits and pieces, there were articles about a man called **JACK BINNS**. He is now officially my hero and when I grow up I am going to be just like him!

Here's a clipping:

WIRELESS HERO SAVES THE DAY

RMS *Republic* radio operator Jack Binns used all of his training when his radio room was left in splinters after a collision with *Florida*.[17] With no way to signal for help BRAVE BINNS found dry batteries and made the repairs needed to send out a CQD distress signal.[18] A signal he continued to tap out for 36 HOURS STRAIGHT until help arrived. In total seven were killed in the accident, a number which would have been much higher if not for Binns' swift action. Binns' bravery was rewarded when he reached land, he was presented with a GOLD WATCH by GUGLIELMO MARCONI HIMSELF!

Lucky Ronald for getting the chance to have a job like that! Also, it shows that you really don't need to worry about sailing across the Atlantic. The ocean is so **FULL OF SHIPS** and they can all radio each other whenever they like. Even if your ship were to crash into anything, like Republic did, the operator could just radio a nearby ship for help.

We'll be setting off back to Cornwall next week. Dad said he and your dad had a few things they wanted to fix on your house and **BITS AND BOBS** to sell and then we will be on our way. I still wish you were coming with us.

William

---

17 The collision took place on 23 January 1909.
18 CQD was the international distress signal before SOS was introduced.

Dear William,

I've been thinking, perhaps you could be called **DASH**? William takes so long to tap out in Morse. I think it makes sense too, because you are always in such a hurry to do everything and racing here and there. '**DOT AND DASH**' has a bit of a ring to it, doesn't it?

Looking forward to you getting back to Cornwall and telling me more about Jack Binns and the Marconi School. It does seem **RIDICULOUS** that women can't enrol in the school. Mother agrees and said that she hopes when I grow up all these silly rules about what women can and can't do will have changed. **LET'S HOPE SO!**[19]

Do you think there is a chance that you could sail on Titanic or Olympic? They probably won't be ready, but wouldn't it be so **AMAZING** after your Uncle Michael worked so hard on building them?

I wish we could come with you, but Tom and I need to stay back and help Mother with Ginny and selling the house. I think she's a bit worried about the trip. But I'm expecting an **AMAZING** apple farm to have appeared by the time we arrive! We're counting on you.

---

19 In 1911 the world was very different for women and girls than the one we know today. In the United Kingdom, women were not allowed to study or graduate from many universities and they were not allowed to vote in elections. After a long campaign, some women were granted the right to vote in 1918, however women were not allowed to vote on the same terms as men until 1928.

I hope the goodbyes to your family in Belfast aren't too sad. I don't know how I am going to say goodbye to Grandma and Grandad. And Meg, too. Mother says they have cats in America, but I know I will never find a cat like Meg.

I'm trying not to think about it.

I'll make sure Grandma bakes you a **BIG BATCH** of fairing biscuits for when you get back.[20] I'd make them myself, but you know what she's like with that secret recipe. Perhaps she will even make you some to take across the Atlantic!

See you soon,

Dot

S S S S S S S

DASH IS THAT YOU?

S S S S S

DASH?

20 A delicious kind of Cornish biscuit. See page 109 for the secret recipe.

S S S S

WILL YOU STOP HISSING AT ME!

I'M BEING MARCONI! I'M SENDING
THE LETTER S, LIKE HE DID TO
NEWFOUNDLAND.

YOU'RE SO SILLY.

DON'T YOU MEAN S S S S S SILLY?

STOP IT.

DON'T YOU MEAN S S S S STOP IT?

S S S S STOP IT. OKAY,
THIS IS GREAT.

ISN'T IT?

YES. I JUST SAID!

TELL YOUR GRAN I'LL BE OVER
FOR DINNER IN 10 MINUTES.

I WILL. I CAN'T BELIEVE YOU LEAVE
FOR THE BOAT TOMORROW.

I KNOW. BEFORE CHRISTMAS, TOO!

YOU'LL TELL ME ALL ABOUT IT WON'T YOU?
AND YOU'LL LOOK AFTER FATHER?

NO. I WILL PUSH HIM OVER-
BOARD AND NEVER SPEAK TO
YOU AGAIN. ANY MORE DAFT
QUESTIONS?

WHY AM I GOING TO MISS YOU
WHEN YOU ARE SO OBNOXIOUS?

DON'T ASK ME.

I JUST DID.
ARE YOU EXCITED? SHAME IT'S NOT
TITANIC.

CAN'T BE HELPED. IF I CAN'T
SAIL ON THE BIGGEST, I AM
HAPPY TO BE ON THE FASTEST.
RMS MAURETANIA.

PERHAPS YOU'LL SET A RECORD.

TOM WOULD LIKE THAT.

HE WOULD.

I'VE GOT TO GET READY FOR
DINNER. BE THERE IN TEN.

SEE YOU THEN. AND THEN
NOT FOR AGES. SOB.

DON'T BE SOPPY.

Dear Dot,

WE ARE HERE! It was a smooth crossing. I was **GUTTED** we didn't get to sail on the Mauretania after all! According to our agent the Mauretania broke free of her moorings[21] and was too damaged to make the trip. I'd hoped that if we were not able to sail on one of the **LARGEST SHIPS** (RMS Olympic or RMS Titanic) we would at least get to travel on the **FASTEST SHIP**. The Mauretania was going to attempt to sail from Southampton to New York and back in just twelve days!

We sailed on the Lusitania instead, which is **STILL** exciting, but it would have been amazing to be part of a **NEW SPEED RECORD**.

At least I had some **PRESENTS** to cheer me up. Don't tell your grandma, but the tin of fairings she sent with me to enjoy at Christmas didn't make it beyond the boat train! I did manage not to open your present though, which I thought was pretty amazing of me. Are you **IMPRESSED**? I am!

The Lusitania was comfortable enough. I shared a second-class cabin with both our dads. I know you told me your dad snored, but you **DID NOT** tell me he snored **THAT** loudly. My father snores too. Between them and the engines I was lucky if I got any sleep on the entire voyage.

21 Ropes that hold a boat in place.

The food was good, and there was lots of it. My favourite thing was **BREAKFAST**. I had pancakes every day with lots of butter, **MAPLE SYRUP** and bacon. I'm sure I won't be eating as well as that for a while with the dads at the stove. I don't think I've seen your dad make so much as a pot of tea before. My dad is a bit better, having looked after Mother for so long, but I don't think he's ever made anything you'd call "delicious."[22] I'm sure I'll be as thin as a rake by the time you get here. Either that, or a chef.

DINE WITH DASH

PAD'S DUDS

22 In 1911, unlike today, cooking within the home was considered women's work. Ugh!

Before we sailed into New York, doctors boarded the ship to give us the once over. The doctor checking me was worried that my eyes looked red. He got out this **HORRIBLE HOOKED INSTRUMENT** to examine them. I told him my eyes were red from **NOT GETTING ENOUGH SLEEP** with all the snoring in our state room. He laughed. He was looking for a disease called trachoma which causes blindness. Luckily I don't have it. People who do have it are **NOT ALLOWED** to enter the country.

The doctors don't examine everyone on board. It's just the 'cabin classes' in first and second. The third-class and steerage passengers go to a place called **ELLIS ISLAND**[23] where they get given lots of tests to make sure they are healthy. If they don't pass the examinations, they are **SENT BACK** to where they started their journeys. He said children who were older than twelve that failed the medical tests could be **SENT BACK ALONE**, but children under twelve had to be accompanied by an adult.

23 Ellis Island in New York Bay was an immigration inspection station. People arriving to start a new life in the United States were given health inspections here and were either admitted to the US if they passed the inspection or hospitalized or sent home if they did not. It is thought over 12 million immigrants passed through Ellis Island while it was in operation.

I can't imagine how disappointed I would be, thinking I was about to start a new life, only to be turned around and sent home.

After my examination, I headed out on deck. The railings were lined with passengers - it looked like the whole ship had come out to watch our arrival into New York. The **STATUE OF LIBERTY** was something special. I can't wait for you to see her. She looked like some kind of **GODDESS** from my book of Greek myths, towering over us. It felt as though she

Welcome to your new home!

was signalling to all on board how welcome they were and telling them what **BIG ADVENTURES** lay ahead of them. I'm not sure I will ever forget it. We had arrived in America and it was just sinking in that this was our new home.

We're going to be Americans!

New York is **BIG** - and busy! The buildings are so tall that when you look up, the tops of them seem to be **LOST IN THE CLOUDS**. The streets are full of people, streetcars, motor cars and horses and carts. Everyone has to shout to be heard over the noise.

It makes me miss home. I'm not sure I like it here at all, but we're only staying a couple of nights at the Star Hotel on Clarkson Street.

Your dad said it's where all the Cornish people stay when they come to America. He said people coming to America from the same place like to help each other out. He is hoping that they will help us find where to buy the things we need before we head out to the orchard. I can't wait to see it now. I tell you one thing for sure if New York doesn't have what we need, **WE DON'T NEED IT**. It seems to have **EVERYTHING**.

We are heading upstate to the orchard tomorrow. Dad said he'd heard that the house was a bit of a **MESS**. I hope we can make things nice for Christmas, though I don't hold out much hope of a good Christmas dinner! I hope you have a jolly time!

Merry Christmas!

Dash

Dear Dash,

I am so happy to hear you arrived! I am sorry you didn't get
to travel on the Mauritania. That does seem like bad luck.
I know you like **SPEED**! If it is faster than the Lusitania it
would be **EVEN LOUDER**, though you might not have been
able to notice that over all the **SNORING**. I mentioned that
to Mother and she found it hilarious. Father does snore
TERRIBLY. I think it will be the one thing she **DOES NOT MISS**
while they are apart.

Christmas wasn't the same without Father or you and
your dad. But we did our best to have a nice time, seeing as
it will be our last Christmas with Grandma and Grandad for a
while, maybe even **FOR EVER**. Grandma gave me a beautiful
leather wallet to keep all my writing paper in. She said it was
for all my future **ADVENTURES**. I can use it to collect bits
and pieces from the journey when we go! Grandad gave me
a book about how to set up my own radio. Let's work on it
together when I get there!

Let me know what the orchard is like when you arrive.
Are there apples everywhere you look? I suppose not in
January. Is the weather different? It is very **GREY** here.

And **WET**. Is your **RADIO** set up? I've been listening out for your call sign. Grandad said he'd eat his hat if we manage it.

No news of a sale just yet. Grandma is **GLAD** as she doesn't want us to go. She is being good about it, but I can tell she is sad. It will be strange not living so close to them anymore. I told Mother I might not **MISS THEM** so much if I could bring Meg with us but she says Meg will be good company for them. And besides, she doesn't want to travel across the Atlantic alone with three children and **ALL OUR WORLDLY GOODS** as well as a cat. I pointed out that she wouldn't be alone if she had us with her and she rolled her eyes. Perhaps I will be able to sneak Meg in my trunk.

Can you explain to me, Madam, why your trunk is purring?

Hope to see you soon,

Dot

Dear Dot,

Thank you for my present - **A CHRISTMAS PUDDING**! I wanted to gobble it all up in a flash, but we shared it. It was so yummy and when I shut my eyes I could just about imagine that I was in England plotting how to **SWIPE** an extra bit off your plate. Just as well I am here, eh?

We took the train most of the way to West Ridge (that's the name of the orchard but Dad said we could think of another name if we like. Have a think!) Then a kind farmer, Mr Johnson, drove us out the rest of the way in his buggy. He said all the farms around here were busy because New York City was **GROWING FAST** and **ALWAYS HUNGRY**. He said it would be hard work, but he hoped we'd like it here.

The house was a bit more run down than we expected, but Dad said it shouldn't take too long to get it looking shipshape. Your father said he would settle for **HOUSE-SHAPED**, as would I. I don't fancy sharing a room with them for any longer than I have to. I want my own door to **BLOCK OUT THE SNORING**, please. In fact, the sooner we fix up the lodge down the road for Dad and I the better.

One thing that is different here is the sky. It just seems **BIGGER**. In Cornwall, you always feel near to the sea, but here the land seems to go on for ever.

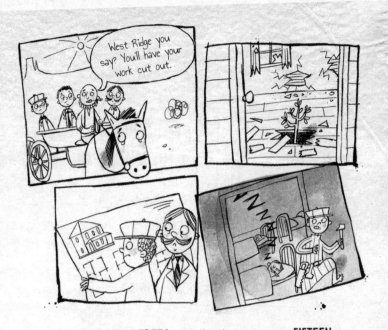

There are **200 APPLE TREES** here already which grow **FIFTEEN DIFFERENT TYPES OF APPLE**! Who knew there were that many types of apple? Your father wants to grow other fruit, too. But first, we're going to focus on restarting the apple business, as well as tidying up the house ready for when you and the rest of your family arrive! I think you will like it here. I can't imagine us ever owning this much land in England. I feel like quite the **LORD OF THE MANOR**. Although I expect most lords aren't expected to mend roofs or prune fruit trees.

Oh! And **I'VE ALREADY MADE A FRIEND**. His name is Harry and he's the son of the farmer who drove us from the station. He lives on the next farm. He has a **RADIO**, too and he's going to help me set up mine. He and his friends have a club called the **"TELEGRAPH TEAM"**.

They go on all sorts of missions together – they even had to **RUN AWAY FROM A BEAR** once! I've not seen a bear, I don't know what I'd do if I did.

Dad's going to let me go with Harry and his friends on a mission next week. I think he will be glad to have me out of his hair! It will be fun to explore the area properly, even if it is a bit **TOO COLD** to do anything like swimming or camping.

From,

Dash

Fairing House

Cornwall

Dear Dash,

You better get a move on fixing up West Ridge because **THE HOUSE IS SOLD**! Mother is so relieved, she's missing Father terribly and is worried Ginny won't recognize him anymore. We're travelling to Southampton by train and will then board a steamer. I'm hoping we will be there in **NO TIME**.

We've been a bit delayed leaving. The coal strike means there isn't enough fuel to go around for all the scheduled trips. The liners are having to scramble coal together from all the ships for each passage. I'm annoyed that there has been a delay but it means - drum roll please - we will be travelling on **RMS TITANIC**!

Mother is very excited, as is **EVERYONE SHE HAS TOLD**. Which is pretty much the **WHOLE** of Cornwall and Tom is just as bad. I can't believe we're going to be on its **MAIDEN VOYAGE**! We will be travelling second class, like you and Father did, but apparently second-class cabins on Titanic are as good as **FIRST-CLASS CABINS** on the Cunard liners, so I will happily spend an extra day at sea if it means swanning about in the lap of luxury.

Oh, and apparently they call cabins, staterooms according the to the brochure. "Stateroom" sounds ever so grand, doesn't it?

Mother is running about packing "**ALL OUR WORLDLY GOODS**".

I don't know how I will say goodbye to Grandma and Grandad! And Meg! But I am so **EXCITED** to see you and Father. I can't wait to hear more about the Telegraph Team, too.

Here's to a smooth crossing. If you want to wish me 'Bon Voyage' you'll have to get your letter to me, quick!

See you soon,

Dot

Dear Dot,

WOW! The Titanic! I am sea-green with envy. I was the one who got to see it launch, **REMEMBER**?

Hooray! Soon you'll be on your way. I can't wait for you to get here. I have been trying to send you messages on the radio. I can message Harry and some of the others, Walter and Alex, but Alex said that we'd need a **MUCH BIGGER** aerial and it would have to be much higher to reach you. Our aerial stretches between the two chimneys of the house, (yes we have a roof now). Walter says he's received signals from ships in the Atlantic before, but I'm not sure if I believe him. I'll have to give it a try when you are sailing!

I've been playing out with Harry and his team a fair bit lately. They are great fun! We radio each other about when we are going to meet and **STAY OUT ALL DAY**. They've got an old shed for a den and we build a fire so it can get quite cosy. Don't worry, I've told them all about you.

Alex is **THRILLED** that there will be another girl in the group. Harry and Walter are glad you are coming, because not only do you know **MORSE CODE** (they think mine needs work. **RUDE**!), but you can also speak French which might come in handy on our missions.

41

Everyone is excited that you are on Titanic. So excited, in fact, they want you to perform your **VERY OWN SECRET MISSION** on board before you even meet the team. Like all of our missions, it is a **SECRET**, so make sure you **DO NOT OPEN** until you are on board.

We're excited that we will be getting a real-life **MISSION REPORT** from the maiden voyage of the **TITANIC**. To think, there I was at the launch and you will be there for its **FIRST** transatlantic voyage. You are a **LUCKY** thing.

I'd wish you a smooth crossing, but on Titanic that is pretty much **GUARANTEED**. And it will be peaceful too, without your dad shaking your stateroom with his **SNORING** all night!

24 Help me! Help me! There's a bear!

Oh, and I had something to add to your mission. Please could you bring some of your grandma's biscuits for me and the Telegraph Team? Try and persuade her to give you the recipe. Then we can learn to make them, and bring a bit of Cornwall to America! **WE COULD SELL THEM!**

I can't wait until you get here so I don't have to bother writing letters anymore. I will be able to radio you whenever I like. Or even better, I can just **RUN DOWN THE ROAD**. Dad and I are at the lodge now. It's small but comfortable and not far at all!

Say hello and goodbye to your grandparents (and Meg) for me. Please tell your grandad that, one day when my signal is strong enough, I will send him a radiotelegraphy message.

Bon Voyage![25] (Though I can't imagine a voyage more 'bon' than one aboard Titanic.)

Dash

---

[25] 'Good journey' in French. For some unknown reason grown-ups like to say this in French when people travel on ships.

Dear Dash,

I thought you'd be jealous! Thank you for the **SECRET MISSION**. I can't wait to open it. I've not stopped wondering what is in it. I hope you are not asking me to get up to any mischief!

We have "**ALL OUR WORLDLY GOODS**" packed, minus Meg. I was so sad to say goodbye.

If only I could take you with me! I will never forget you.

But it's goodbye for 'miaow'.

You'll be pleased to know our luggage includes a tin of fairings from Grandma for you and the team. I hope they survive the trip! Tom has had his eye on them, and so has Ginny. She's got a tooth coming through, and I think she'd like to **GNAW** on a biscuit or two.

Not to worry though, Grandma gave me some new writing paper for the leather wallet she gave me at Christmas and a new pen so that I could write to her when we arrive in New York. I opened it up and saw the front sheet had a note. It was her **SECRET RECIPE**! I was so happy I cried. It was really sad to say goodbye, but it will be so lovely to be able to have a little taste of home.

We set sail tomorrow. We are staying at a guest house tonight, but I don't think I will be able to sleep, and not just because we all have to share a room and Tom has inherited Dad's snoring, but also because I am too **EXCITED**.

I will send this letter before we board. I thought it could be like a race. It will be fun to see whether I arrive before it does! Who knows, if it manages to hop in a sack bound for one of the faster Cunard ships. it may well!

Let the race begin! Full steam ahead!

Dot

P.S. I will try and send you a postcard from Cherbourg or Queenstown[26] too, but I think the "mission report" is going to keep me busy.

---

26 Port on the coast of Ireland now named Cobh.

SECRET MISSION
DO NOT OPEN UNTIL YOU ARE ON BOARD TITANIC

Dear Dot,

You are now on board Titanic. I knew you would wait. I would not have been able to wait. I **DO NOT** like waiting one little bit, as you know!

As promised, here is your first mission from the **TELEGRAPH TEAM**. It will not be easy, but should you choose to accept this challenge, know you will have earned your place in the team. (They'll let you in anyway, but this would be a truly triumphant start.)

TELEGRAPH TEAM MISSION OBJECTIVE FOR
AGENT ~~DOTTY~~ DOROTHY BAXTER

The agent (that's you) must find out everything she can about the ship and those on board.

MISSION TASKS

1. EXPLORE THE SHIP
Keep a record of everywhere you manage to visit. We want to know **EVERYTHING ABOUT THE SHIP**. You get bonus points (we're not really scoring) if you manage to get a good look at the swimming pool and a go on the electric camel.

2. COLLECT SOUVENIRS

Any interesting bits and pieces from the voyage that you can: menus, stationery, napkins, postcards. This is Titanic's maiden voyage, so these are **VALUABLE** historical artefacts.

3. SEND A MARCONIGRAM FROM THE SHIP

Try to visit the Marconi room and speak to the Marconi officer. The Telegraph Team wants to know the **LATEST NEWS** in radio technology. Find out about the ship's range and the kind of messages people are sending on board. You get bonus points (again, not scoring) if you get a go at the key yourself.

4. FIND OUT WHO'S ON BOARD

Who are they and why are they travelling on Titanic? If you can speak to the **CAPTAIN** or anyone important, all the better.

5. REFRESHMENTS

Don't let your brother or Ginny eat my biscuits. Try maple syrup. You will **LOVE** it!

6. SECRECY

DO NOT tell anyone about this mission. Except Tom, of course.

7. HAVE A SAFE TRIP!

From,
THE TELEGRAPH TEAM
Dash, Walter, Harry and Alex

MISSION REPORT - DAY ONE
10TH APRIL 1912

MISSION ACCEPTED!
I will collect everything I can and keep it in my leather wallet.

THE SHIP
I said I wanted an **ADVENTURE** and to travel the world - what a way to start! I know you said Titanic was colossal, but that word doesn't seem colossal enough! I'm trying to think of a bigger word but I can't. There should be a new word for it. **SUPER-GI-MUNGUS**, perhaps? I'm not sure what I was expecting when we got to Southampton, but it **DWARFED** all of the other ships.

NEAR MISS
As we pulled out of the dock, Titanic was so steady, the only way you could tell it was moving was the faintest vibration from the three engines down below. I watched all the other ships in Southampton get further and further away as we drifted out to sea. Well, all but one. A ship called SS New York **GOT CLOSER**, sucked in by the pull of Titanic through the water. I thought it would **SMASH** right into us!

Titanic's sister ship Olympic had a similar thing happen on one of her first voyages. Olympic **ALMOST SANK** another ship by pulling it into a collision. Olympic was so badly damaged that she took weeks to fix! Yikes!

The crew used Titanic's port propeller to create a wash which pushed SS New York away. Then the tugboats got the ships under control and we were soon on our way. Although, I suppose if we had sunk, it wouldn't be so bad as we were near land. Tom said this would be **ALMOST IMPOSSIBLE** (really, he has read **EVERYTHING**) as the Olympic-class liners are **PRACTICALLY UNSINKABLE**. If the incident with Olympic proved anything, it is that a ship like Titanic can sustain a lot of **DAMAGE** and stay afloat. He drew a picture of the hull on a napkin as he explained why it would be almost impossible for Titanic to sink.

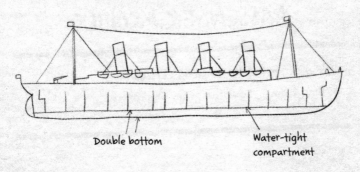

Double bottom   Water-tight
                                 compartment

A lady who was listening leaned in to see Tom's drawing.[27]

"**ALMOST IMPOSSIBLE**, is a long way from **IMPOSSIBLE**," she said. She was spooked by the near-miss with SS New York. The lady's daughter was called Eva Hart (don't you think that is a lovely name?) I spoke to her a bit later on.

27 *Titanic* passenger Esther Hart, travelling in second class with her family was terrified of the voyage.

She said her father had been excited about the trip for ages and wasn't scared one bit, but that her mother had a bad feeling about the voyage. She said her mother thought it was **DANGEROUS** that a ship of this size not have enough lifeboats for all on board. She said her mother was so frightened that she had vowed not to put on her nightclothes while on board in case she needed to make a **MAD DASH** to a lifeboat. She was just going to sit up on her bunk at night and sleep during the day.

PASSENGER PROFILE

Passenger ticket for the **RMS TITANIC**
Sailing from: Southampton, England

Passenger name: Eva Hart
Date of Birth: 31st January 1905
Travelling to: Winnipeg, Canada

Notes: Eva's father is excited about being on Titanic, apparently. Eva's mother is convinced something terrible is going to happen and that we are all doomed. Eva seems kind and friendly.

I asked Tom whether it was true that there weren't enough lifeboats for everyone. He said it was true, but that it had as many as was expected of ships this size and that if there was enough for everyone the deck would be **CHOCK A BLOCK** with them. He said ships like Titanic didn't need more lifeboats because:

A) they were very unlikely to sink

and

B) even if Titanic were to start sinking (and it wouldn't) the Atlantic Ocean is so busy with ships going here and there that Titanic would be able to **RADIO FOR HELP**. We would be picked up in **NO TIME**.

Mother stopped him, and said that all the talk about sinking and lifeboats was making her feel **QUEASY**. I hope I get to spend more time with Eva on board. She was ever so nice and chatty and has lovely dark hair.

ACCOMMODATIONS

Our cabin is **HEAVENLY**! Everything on Titanic is **BRAND NEW**. You can tell, some parts of the ship smell of **NEW PAINT**! I am going to make sure to hop into bed first so that I can be the very, very first to lie in it. It would be such a shame to have **ALMOST** been the first.

No one ever remembers the almost first to do something. Imagine travelling on Titanic's **SECOND VOYAGE**.

I'm sharing the bottom bunk with Mother and Tom is up top. There is a little sofa and it cleverly turns into another bed that Ginny can fit on just fine. We're going to be **EXTREMELY** comfortable!

We have our own basin with hot and cold water, and a little writing desk which is where I am sitting **RIGHT NOW**. It is **SO FANCY**, though another passenger said that it is nothing compared to some of the **FIRST-CLASS** staterooms that have their own bathrooms, telephones and even their own balconies looking out over the ocean! I am going to do my best to get in and see one for the team. I will report back when I find a way.

That's all for now, as **LOVELY** as our cabin is, I'm not going to be able to complete much of my mission report sat here in my room.

We are about to arrive in Cherbourg to pick up more passengers. Can you believe it, some poor passengers are actually leaving the ship at Cherbourg?[28] What **BAD LUCK**!

28 There were 24 passengers who disembarked *Titanic* at Cherbourg, France.

MISSION REPORT - DAY TWO - 17TH APRIL 1912

Just got back to the cabin after eating breakfast and walking Ginny on deck. I have so much to report!

FOOD
For breakfast I had buckwheat pancakes with **MAPLE SYRUP**. It is **DELICIOUS**! The steward said it is popular in America. If that is true, I am determined I will eat it **EVERY DAY** when I get there. Though I'm not sure I believe him when he said it came from **TREE SAP**?!![29]

Can you believe Mother had grilled ox kidneys with bacon!? Grown-ups can be exceptionally strange sometimes. I don't like eating meat that has done a "job" - no heart, liver, brains ... ugh. I am going to stop there, before I start to think I am **SEASICK**.

The dining room is lovely. Crisp white tablecloths and plates and cloth napkins with "White Star Line" written on them. We sit at tables of eight, and I was annoyed to discover that you have to sit at the same table for **EVERY** meal. I was hoping mealtimes would be the perfect time to talk to other passengers. Our table seems **JOLLY** though so I can't complain.

---

29 It is true. Maple syrup is made from the sap of the sugar maple tree, common in North America.

I know I said Tom had become an **OLYMPIC-CLASS BORE** with all his steamship studying, but he came in **EXTREMELY HANDY** while I was walking Ginny on the deck this morning. In fact, he has helped me with **MY MISSION** in a way I could never have expected. It may kill me to tell him that, but I will because he would hate to miss the adventure.

A man was talking **VERY LOUDLY** about how we were on the **BIGGEST** and **FASTEST** boat the world had ever seen. Have you ever noticed how the people who explain things in the **LOUDEST VOICES** tend to know the **LEAST** about the subject they are talking about? Tom is never loud, but he **KNOWS HIS STUFF**. This man did not, so I thought I would help him out.

"Titanic is a **WONDERFUL** ship, but it is neither the **BIGGEST**, nor the **FASTEST**. Titanic is the same size as her sister Olympic and I've heard the Mauretania is **MUCH** faster."

I heard a **BIG LAUGH** behind me and turned around. I wanted the deck to swallow me up, or to hop over the side into the freezing Atlantic Ocean. It was **CAPTAIN SMITH** himself! He asked if I was **UNIMPRESSED** by Titanic.

"It's a little unfair to say Titanic can't be as fast as Mauretania when we haven't even completed the journey," he said. "I'll be going **FULL-STEAM AHEAD** after the stop at Queenstown, then you'll see what Titanic can really do!"

He looked just as you would imagine a ship's captain to, with a white beard and perfectly ironed uniform. He reminded me a bit of Father Christmas! I told him that I was **VERY IMPRESSED** with the ship. He's going to arrange for the steward to take me on a tour! I can't wait. I told him I really wanted to see the **MARCONI ROOM**, and perhaps the **SWIMMING POOL**. He laughed again and said with so much water in the Atlantic he couldn't think what would be so interesting about a swimming pool.

I assured him that since it was only the second ship ever to set sail with one on board (another Tom fact), it was very interesting indeed.

Big white ship's captain beard

He has medals and everything!

Shiny buttons

Really important stripes on sleeves

CAPTAIN PROFILE

Name: Edward John Smith

Date of Birth: 27th January 1850

Age: 62

Boarded: Southampton

First command: 1877, aged 26

First command White Star Line: 1887

Number of voyages captained for the White Star Line: 18

Years of experience: 43

Notes: Looks a bit like Father Christmas. Has a large Russian wolfhound called Ben. (I miss Meg. Can you tell?)

We are about to pull into Queenstown now. I wonder if anyone will be leaving the ship at Queenstown?[30] I think the journey to New York could take twice as long and I still wouldn't have explored half the places I want to. If I wasn't so excited to see you and Father I might try and stow-away for the return trip.

30 Seven passengers disembarked *Titanic* at Queenstown, Ireland.

I think my **FAVOURITE** part of the **TELEGRAPH TEAM MISSION** is speaking to other passengers and finding out about where they are going. There are so many people on board - people from **ALL OVER THE WORLD**. I've met passengers from Germany, Russia, Norway and some from countries I bet you've never heard of before. So many of these people are on their way to a **NEW LIFE** in America and Canada, just like us! I was excited when we stopped in Cherbourg, as I was looking forward to practising my French with some real French people!

A lovely family called the Laroches came on board. They have two **ADORABLE** little girls. The youngest looks about the same age as Ginny, and I thought it would be nice if they were friends, so I went and introduced myself straight away. They probably thought I was terribly odd!

PASSENGER PROFILES

Name: Mrs Juliette Laroche

Date of Birth: 20th October 1889

Travelling to: Haiti

Boarded: Cherbourg, France

Name: Mr Joseph Philippe Mercier Laroche
Date of Birth: 26th May 1886
Travelling to: Haiti
Boarded: Cherbourg, France
Occupation: Engineer

Notes: Unable to find work in France. Likes Titanic because the whole family is able to travel and eat together.

Name: Miss Simonne Laroche
Date of Birth: 19th February 1909
Travelling to: Haiti
Boarded: Cherbourg, France

Notes: Sweet little girl who likes to play with Ginny.

Name: Miss Louise Laroche
Date of Birth: 2nd July 1910
Travelling to: Haiti
Boarded: Cherbourg, France

Notes: Very sweet, even littler, girl. I wish they were moving to New York.

They are moving to Haiti, as Mr Laroche had trouble finding work in Paris. His wife thinks this is because people there are closed minded and don't want to hire a dark-skinned person.

Mr Laroche was born in Haiti so they are heading back there so he can look for a job. They were supposed to travel on another ship, but children in second class had to eat in a nursery and were **NOT ALLOWED** to join their parents in the main dining room, which sounded a bit mean. I would hate it if Ginny or I weren't allowed to eat with Mother. I think they made the right decision![31] The girls are so sweet when they play with Ginny. Mrs Laroche said my French was **VERY GOOD** which was kind of her.

No sign of the steward or the tour today. I do hope Captain Smith remembered. I was so **EXCITED**!

MISSION REPORT - DAY FOUR - 13TH APRIL 1912

Captain Smith **DID** remember after all. A steward[32] named Albert called at our stateroom after lunch. He had been sent

---

31 It was common for children in well-to-do families to have their meals in the nursery both at home and on board ships. This was probably so they didn't disturb the grown-ups' boring conversations.

32 A steward is someone who would look after passengers on the ship.

by Captain Smith to take us on a tour of the ship. Tom, if you can believe it, was **SPEECHLESS**. Albert said he could come along, too. Mother said she would be glad of the peace and quiet. Ginny had finally settled down for a nap - she's been sleeping badly. I don't think she likes travelling much!

A TITANIC TOUR

The first thing we wanted to see was the **MARCONI ROOM** which was up on the boat deck. To get to the boat deck we went up in a lift. The lifts are like wooden cupboards with two cage-like doors. You have to pull both the doors closed before the lift will move and then you press the button of the deck you want to go to and then ping! There you are. **BRILLIANT**! We took the lift up to the boat deck.

MARCONI ROOM

The Marconi room was smaller than I expected it to be. I'm not sure why I thought it would be huge - radio equipment doesn't take up much space, but when I saw the aerial running the whole length of the ship, part of me thought it would go into an enormous radio because everything on Titanic is bigger ... it's **TITANIC**.[33] HA! I can't believe I just thought of that!

The operator didn't have much time to talk. Everyone on board is so **EXCITED** that they can send messages back home that the operator spends hours and hours every day sending silly things

33 The word '*Titanic*' means really big and strong.

like: "Set off safe and sound. Marvellous ship. See you soon!"
and "Received your message. See you in New York as planned!".
There are two operators that take it in turns, so that there
is **ALWAYS** someone at the radio. The man currently on shift
was called Jack. Albert let Tom and I hang around, quietly
examining the equipment until Jack had finished his shift, so
we could chat a little longer.

PASSENGER PROFILES

Name: Jack Phillips

Date of Birth: 11th April 1887

Boarded: Belfast

Occupation: Marconi Operator

Notes: Jack had his twenty-fifth birthday while on board.
He and the other operator, Harold Bride had a feast of first-
class pastries to celebrate! I wish we'd dropped in then. Yum!

Jack used to work at the post office just like your cousin
Ronald. He said the **MARCONI SCHOOL** was hard work, but
worth it because now he's been an operator on all kinds of
ships, including Mauretania and Lusitania. He said he had just
come off his shift and needed to rest as he would be back at
his post from 8 p.m. to 2 a.m.

I asked if I could send a message and he said yes, just this once!

I hope you get it, it was so fun filling in the little form and handing it over. I even wrote it out in Morse code underneath so he could see **I KNEW MY STUFF**. Mother had given me a little spending money, and I offered it, but Jack just gave me a wink and said not to worry about it. Jack passed it to the other radio operator who had just started his shift, Harold Bride. When he saw the Morse, he gave me a smile and seemed impressed.

Date: 13th April 1912

The Marconi International Marine Communication Co., Ltd

Handed in at: TITANIC	Charges to Pay.	
	Total	

"DASH. IN THE MARCONI ROOM. YOU WOULD LOVE IT. MISSION ALMOST COMPLETE. SEE YOU SOON. DOT. NOT DOTTY."

Maybe the Telegraph Team could pick up messages from steamships. I hope you are listening out for us! After our chat, Harold started sending messages from passengers again, and trying to get other ships to clear the line. Albert said that as well as sending and receiving messages for passengers, the Marconi operators also received messages from other ships in the area about sailing conditions such as storm warnings or if anyone spots any icebergs. Tom and I were **SURPRISED** Harold was asking the other ships to clear his line so he could send passenger messages. Messages from other ships sounded more important. But what do I know?[34]

How far can you receive messages?

During the day, 250 miles, but at night as far as 2,000 miles!

PASSENGER PROFILES

Name: Harold Bride

Date of Birth: 11th January 1890

Boarded: Belfast

Occupation: Assistant Marconi Operator

Notes: As an employee of the Marconi company, he receives monthly wages.

I'm not sure I'd like to be a radio operator. It looks like hard and tiring work and you don't get the chance to speak to

34 Radio operators were not employed by the White Star Line but by the Marconi Company. They did send and receive messages to and from other ships, but were primarily there to send and receive passenger messages for profit. There was a lot of pressure for operators to get through as many of these as possible. On the night RMS *Titanic* sank, the radio operator Jack Phillips hastily brushed off a warning from a nearby ship called *Californian*, warning him that *Titanic* was entering an ice field. Ten minutes later, *Titanic* struck an iceberg.

anyone, just sleep and pass on messages. But if that is what you and Ronald have your hearts set on, their uniforms are very smart and they do get to sail all over the world. And I like the idea of first-class pastries for my birthday. When I travel the world though I want to speak to **REAL PEOPLE** like I have been doing for my mission report. Perhaps I should be a spy!

Albert said it was time to move on and asked where we would like to go next. I yelled, "the **SWIMMING POOL**!" just as Tom shouted, "the **ENGINES**!"

Albert laughed and said it was going to be a long walk! But what a walk it was. We took the **GRAND STAIRCASE** all the way down. Normally second-class passengers don't get to see this area as it is for **FIRST-CLASS PASSENGERS ONLY**, but if we were on best behaviour, Albert thought it would be fine.

This must have been what your Uncle Michael was talking about at the launch. There was polished wood as far as the eye could see, finely carved and shining in the light of an **ENORMOUS** glass dome above it. It looked like something you'd see in a royal palace or a museum, not on a ship.

On the way to the swimming pool, we passed the gymnasium. Albert asked if we would like to take a look. He said children from first class were allowed to play in there in the afternoons so we wouldn't be **DISTURBING ANY GROWN-UPS**. What a strange room! It was filled with all types of wooden and metal contraptions. I wouldn't have known what they were for if there wasn't a boy sitting astride what looked a bit like a bicycle. He was pedalling away, but he **WASN'T GOING ANYWHERE**!

I pointed at another funny looking machine and asked Albert what it did and he said it was an **ELECTRIC CAMEL** and asked whether I would like to give it a try. **YES, PLEASE**! Tom was already dodging imaginary blows from a leather punching bag, so I climbed on.

What a funny thing! Once I was on, Albert flicked a switch and it started bucking up and down, **A BIT LIKE RIDING A HORSE**. It was fun, but I can't say it was good exercise because it felt like the camel was doing most of the work. I asked Albert what it was for and he said he'd heard it was **GOOD FOR THE LIVER**!

Tom then ran to the middle and sat on a sliding seat in the middle of the room and took hold of the two wooden poles mounted to the floor on either side of the seat.

The poles were oars! I took the seat behind Tom. Now this was **GOOD EXERCISE**! It was fun, but it did feel strange getting so **OUT OF BREATH** without moving anywhere!

It was time to get going so we followed Albert out of the gym. We passed lots of **WELL-DRESSED** passengers on the stairs, but I didn't think I dared speak to any of them until one came and spoke to Albert! He introduced himself as Victor and said he worked for a man called Mr Benjamin Guggenheim and that Mr Guggenheim had **COMPLAINED** that there was something funny about the water that came to his bathtub and could Albert come and take a look.

Albert agreed and said **WE COULD COME TOO** if we stayed close and didn't touch anything. I didn't mind staying close **AT ALL**. This was our chance to have a look at a room in first class.

I hope you don't mind, but I told Victor about the mission report and asked if he would answer a few questions.

Victor was nice, he had short dark hair, dark skin and wore a **FANCY** suit. He said he was born in Liverpool and that his father was a cotton merchant from Italy and that his mother was Egyptian. He said he went to boarding school in Yorkshire but now **LIVED IN AMERICA** working for Mr Guggenheim.

I asked him what New York was like and he said it was a place where **ANYTHING** could happen. He'd left England not much more than a schoolboy and now he was an assistant to one of the **RICHEST** men in the world. **WOW**!

Victor said he was travelling **FIRST CLASS** so that he could see to anything Mr Guggenheim might need **DAY OR NIGHT**. He said Mr Guggenheim's driver was travelling second class as there wasn't much need of a driver while sailing.

PASSENGER PROFILES

Name: Victor Gaitan Andrea Giglio

Date of Birth: 17th June 1888

Boarded: Cherbourg

Occupation: Valet to Mr Benjamin Guggenheim

Notes: Paid his own way to travel to America in 1910 and now works for one of the richest men in the world. Likes to play the piano in his spare time.

Name: Benjamin Guggenheim

Date of Birth: 26th October 1965

Boarded: Cherbourg

Occupation: Businessman

Notes: Nicknamed the "Silver Prince" because he has made so much money from his family's mining business. Victor said he doesn't just have silver mines, but copper and gold and even diamond mines. Even more wow!

Victor and Mr Guggenheim's cabin was **MUCH LARGER** than ours and even more comfortable. It had one big bed and a smaller one, both with quilts and a **COSY SOFA** with electric lamps for reading. At the end of the room there were large brass framed windows that looked out on to the ocean. As well as the main room, there was another small bedroom where Victor slept. I thought the cabin would have its own bathroom, but it didn't, it shared a bathroom with the cabin next door. Albert went in for a quick look and I heard him turn on the taps.

He said there was **NOTHING** wrong with the water and that the baths ran salt water to help conserve fresh water on board. He said fresh water was available from the showers in the **PRIVATE BATHROOMS** of the parlour suites if Mr Guggenheim wanted to book one of them the next time he travelled. Victor said he would let Mr Guggenheim know.

I thanked Victor for helping me with my mission report and told him how **LOVELY** I thought their rooms were. He said I should try and get a look at one of the **PARLOUR SUITES** if I could. He said that would really make my mission report something **SPECIAL**.

I asked Albert if we could look at a parlour suite and he laughed and said he couldn't get in one of them even if he wanted to, but why didn't I go and ask Mr Ismay, the director of White Star Line. He was just over there.

I could tell Albert was joking, but Tom must have missed it, because he **WALKED RIGHT OVER** to Mr Ismay and asked!

Mr Ismay looked **TAKEN ABACK**. Albert looked **HORROR-STRUCK**.

I didn't want to get Albert in trouble so I went over to explain. I told him about you and the **TELEGRAPH TEAM** and how **AMAZED** I was by the ship and that Albert had been asked by Captain Smith to give us a tour.

Mr Ismay looked amused but said, "Well I'll be having words with Captain Smith. Though I suppose if it is for a **REAL-LIFE MISSION REPORT** I should let you take a look." He told Albert to make sure we didn't disturb anything.

PASSENGER PROFILE

Name: Joseph Bruce Ismay

Date of Birth: 12th December 1862

Boarded: Southampton

Occupation: Chairman and managing director of the White Star Line (that's the company that own and operate all of the Olympic-class vessels including Titanic).

Notes: Ismay likes to accompany all of the White Star ships on their first voyage. He said he thinks Olympic and Titanic are the very best.

INSIDE A REAL PARLOUR SUITE - BONUS POINTS PLEASE!!

I thought Mr Guggenheim's rooms were fancy, but Victor was right, it was something special. We turned left into one large bedroom. The room was beautiful. **GLEAMING** wooden panels covered the walls. Everything looked extremely **EXPENSIVE**, I didn't dare touch a thing. Silk drapes surrounded a bed much larger than the one in our room and it looked much softer! We walked through that room into the next which held two of the **MOST GINORMOUS** wardrobes I had ever seen - they were rooms!

I asked Albert, "How many outfits does a person need for a seven-day voyage?"

"Heavens if I know. One of the boys told me, Mrs Cardeza in the other parlour suite had brought with her **14 TRUNKS**, **FOUR SUITCASES** and **THREE CRATES** of baggage for her and her son!" Yikes!

There was a tiled bathroom, with a tub I think would **TEMPT EVEN YOU** to take a bath more than once a week, and the freshwater shower Albert had mentioned before.

The next room, and yes there was a **NEXT ROOM**, was a sitting room with a pretty chairs, a sofa and a fireplace. There were electric lamps and lots of cosy spots where you could sit and read a book **AND** large windows that looked out on to the **OCEAN**. A set of double doors even opened out on to the suite's **VERY OWN PROMENADE DECK**! Outside, there were chairs, a table and even sun loungers where you could **RELAX** and enjoy the view.

I think if we were to have a room like that, I wouldn't want to leave it **EVEN AFTER** arriving in New York! The parlour suite seemed **BIGGER THAN OUR HOUSE**, but more fancy. I can't imagine what Mr Ismay would want with all that space and all those beds just for himself.

PARLOUR PROFILE

Class:	First
Deck:	B
Bedrooms:	2 large with 4 beds in total
Sitting room:	1
Promenade deck:	1 private deck with lots of seats and space to take meals outside.
Bathroom:	1 private bathroom with bath and shower
Wardrobes:	2 large, walk-in
Ticket price:	Free[35]

I was starting to get used to the parlour suite, when Albert said we had to get moving. The swimming pool was down on F deck so we took the lift the rest of the way.

35 As Ismay worked for White Star it is unlikely he would have had to pay for his suite. A passenger named Mrs Cardeza paid £512, 6s to travel in a similar suite, which would be just under £60,000 today!

F Deck is mostly made up of third-class passenger accommodation apart from the racquet court, Turkish baths and **SWIMMING POOL** for first-class passengers and a few second-class staterooms. Oh, and kennels! Can you **BELIEVE** that? I could have brought Meg after all! I couldn't believe it at all. Albert said there were **12 DOGS** of all shapes and sizes in there. He said some first-class passengers even had their pets with them in their cabins. I would **LOVE** to have Meg with me on board. She could help me with my mission, I'm sure!

This parlour suite is purrr-fect!

NOBODY was in the swimming pool when we got there so Albert said we could go in and take a look. The pool is filled with salt water and heated by one of the boiler rooms that was just underneath where we were standing. Tom said the **RIPPLES** on the surface were caused by the vibrations of the engines. He really is useful to have around sometimes.

A sign said that passengers would have to pay to use the pool, but that included the use of a bathing suit. Tom said it seemed a **BIT OF A SWINDLE** to charge people to use a pool after what they had paid to travel first class. Plus, I'm not sure I like the idea of wearing a **USED BATHING SUIT**, but I suppose on the maiden voyage they would be **NICE AND NEW**!

We weren't there long before a first-class passenger wanted to use the pool so we set off for the **ENGINE ROOM**. It was a long walk, but we did stop and chat to a few third-class passengers on our way. We went into a room Albert said was the "general room".[36] It had long tables with benches to sit at. There was even a piano against one wall and windows looking out to the Well Deck.

In the general room, Tom started chatting to a boy who looked about his age and was reading a book with a picture of a boat on the front. The boy's name was Charles. Charles is on board with his mother and father and **FIVE** brothers and sisters. They are on their way to Niagara, New York where his father is going to work at a power station. His uncle has lived there

36 The 'general room' was a place where third-class passengers could pass the time. Here, passengers could talk, play cards and even dance.

for some time and had done very well for himself. Charles said his uncles all chipped in to buy their tickets.

PASSENGER PROFILE

Name: Mr Charles Goodwin

Date of Birth: 22nd May 1897

Boarded: Southampton

Travelling to: Niagara, New York

Notes: Has five brothers and sisters.

"What is third class like?" I asked.

"The food is good," replied Charles. "And the cabins are clean, but they're a bit small. I spend most of my time in the general room or walking on the poop deck."

Like us, he was supposed to be travelling on another steamer but was transferred to Titanic because of the coal strike. He said there were all types of people in third class, from **ALL OVER THE WORLD**. He'd spoken to singers, labourers and even a boxer. Second class doesn't seem anywhere near as **INTERESTING**.

We asked if we could see his cabin and he took us along. It was **VERY** different from Mr Ismay's and even ours. It was **SMALL**, four bunk beds close together separated by a wash basin.

I asked about a bathtub and he said he heard that there was one for men and one for women but that he probably **WOULDN'T BOTHER** having one.[37]

While we were talking, his sister came over carrying a little boy not much younger than Ginny.

"Hello! My name is Jessie and this is Sidney. I've come to put him down for his nap. Poor boy doesn't like this travelling lark." I told her Ginny was the same and we left them to it.

Charles said his whole family slept in that cabin, his mother, father and **FIVE** brothers and sisters.

"I hope we see Charles again," Tom said as we carried on the tour. "It would be nice to have a friend in New York that likes the same kind of books as me."

"And Jessie, too! I wish they were allowed up to second class. Sidney would be a playmate for Ginny too."

I asked Albert if he thought they would be allowed up to second class to visit and Albert said, "Not likely! See these gates?" He unlocked the gates for us to pass through and then locked them behind us. He said the gates were to stop third-class passengers from **WANDERING ABOUT** in second and first class.

---

37 While this may sound really yucky, in 1912 it was totally normal for people to go a week without a bath. Many people believed bathing daily could make you sick.

He said third-class passengers were given health checks for lice and other things before they got on board but with so many people so close together in third class, disease spread quickly. The gates would stop sick people from spreading infection throughout the ship.

We carried on towards the **ENGINE ROOM**. Albert admitted that that he didn't know much about how the engines worked. Tom was **THRILLED**! Any excuse to show off how much he knows!

Tom talked **ON AND ON** about them for ages and in his excitement, he was talking so fast that I'm sure I missed quite a bit, but this is what I gathered. Titanic has a total of **159 FURNACES** which burn lots and lots of coal. The heat from the furnaces is used to make the steam which powers the ship's **THREE ENGINES**. Titanic's engines have **46,000 HORSEPOWER** combined. There are more than a hundred "stokers" on board who have to shovel the coal into the furnaces day and night.

Tom was **EXCITED** to meet one of the stokers and asked him lots of questions about his work.

PASSENGER PROFILE

Name: Mr John Priest

Date of Birth: 31st August 1887

Boarded: Southampton

Occupation: Stoker

Notes: Was on board Olympic when it crashed!

John said Titanic uses as much as **600 TONS OF COAL A DAY**!
The steam from the boilers passes through lots of pipes to
ENORMOUS spinny things called turbines. The steam makes the
turbines spin which helps turn the three big propellers which
people call screws. I'd wondered why people said Titanic was a
"TRIPLE SCREW", it's because the propellers turn like screws,
not that it was only held together by three screws.

How are we supposed to build a ship with just three screws?

That made a lot more sense! Tom asked if it was true that the engines ran at **46,000 HORSE POWER** and John laughed.

"You'd think the engines did all the work!" John said, "Me and the lads shovel up to **600 TONS OF COAL** a day to keep those engines running. People talk about horsepower, but horses have nothing to do with it. Steamships run on manpower."

I asked him whether this was the **BIGGEST** ship he had worked on. "One of them, Miss!" John said. "I worked on **OLYMPIC**, too! I was on board when it was almost sunk."[38] **AMAZING!** Then Albert said we had to go, so we said goodbye to John.

We thanked Albert **VERY MUCH** for the tour once he'd taken us back to our room. As it turns out, we had returned **JUST IN TIME** for dinner and Ginny had since woken from her nap. Must go to bed now or I won't be able to keep my eyes open tomorrow!

MISSION REPORT - DAY FIVE - 14TH APRIL 1912

11.50 P.M.[39]

Sorry I didn't get a chance to write today! The tour yesterday was **SO EXCITING** but Tom and I were tired from all that walking,

---

38 The unsinkable John Priest survived not only the crash on the *Olympic*, but the sinking of the *Titanic* and the sinking of their sister ship *Britannic* when it hit a mine in 1916.
39 *Titanic* struck an iceberg at 11.40 p.m. on 14th April 1912.

so we spent most of our day in the stateroom helping Mother and playing with Ginny. We told Mother **ALL** about the tour and she said she the electric camel sounds terrifying.

I'm writing now because I just woke up to the most **HORRIBLE** scraping sound. It made our whole cabin shake. Tom snuck out to **INVESTIGATE** what happened. I don't know how it didn't wake Mother or Ginny! I suppose if she can sleep through **FATHER'S SNORING** she can sleep through anything. I know we weren't the only ones to hear it because I can hear doors opening and closing and voices in the corridor outside. I wish I could have gone with Tom, but he didn't want to wake Mother or make her worry if she woke up to find us both gone!

MISSION REPORT – DAY SIX – 15TH APRIL 1912

12.10 A.M.

Tom's back. He said the ship struck an **ICEBERG**! He went up to the deck and said there were chunks of ice all over the place. We've decided to wake Mother and Ginny. He said he bumped into Albert who told him to pop his coat and lifejacket on and head back up to the boat deck, just in case.

I'm not too worried. Titanic is **SO BIG**, I can't imagine how massive the iceberg would have to be to sink it. As Tom said it is "practically unsinkable". I better run. Mother is fussing about us buttoning up our coats. You'd think we were babies!

12.30 A.M.

They are loading the lifeboats now. Women and children first. Mother and Ginny got in one of the first. People didn't want to get in them and I can see why. The lifeboats look **TINY** compared to Titanic and **IT IS FREEZING** out on deck. Nobody wants to spend a cold night on a lifeboat when we could be sent back to our cabins any minute. Tom and I ran back to the cabin to get Mother and Ginny the blankets from our room. It's so cold out there Mother thought she might need them! I picked up my mission report, too. In all the **CHAOS**, I'd left it behind! I'll tuck it under my coat to keep it safe ... just in case.

1.00 A.M.

When we got back, their lifeboat had already been lowered. Mother must be so **WORRIED**. We are going to look for another.

1.20 A.M.

The boat is **TILTING** a lot now. Tom says it must have taken on a lot of water. People are starting to think that Titanic might actually sink. As we approached a lifeboat, a man grabbed me and **TOSSED ME IN** like I was a sack of spuds. Tom wondered where I'd gone so I yelled to get his attention but when he tried to climb in after me, he was stopped by one of the crew.

They thought Tom was a **GROWN-UP**! The man loading the boat wouldn't listen when I told them he was just a boy. Tom told me to go. He said he'd find another, but there was **NO WAY** I'd go without him. I climbed out.

83

I didn't know what to do next. That's when I remembered your story about Jack Binns. When the ship he was on was in an **ACCIDENT**, he had to fix the radio before he was able to message other ships for help. It was his **BRAVERY** that saved so many people. I thought about Bride and Phillips in the radio room. They'd know if help was on the way. Perhaps there was something we could do to help. I told Tom and he agreed that we should go to the **MARCONI ROOM** and see what we could do, so that's where we are now. Phillips is at the key. He is tapping out **CQD**[40] to all the boats in the area to see if any are close enough to come to our aid.

Phillips and Bride joked that they should try the **NEW SOS SIGNAL** as it could be their only chance if this is their last voyage. I didn't think it was **FUNNY** at all, but Tom thought it was **HILARIOUS**. How can people make jokes at a time like this?

Phillips hasn't stopped tapping out distress signals, since we came in. Bride said there are ships in the area and they are doing everything they can to contact them. He said one called the **CARPATHIA** has said that it has changed its course and is on its way, but we should get to a lifeboat, quick. He hasn't pushed us out the door though, so we are staying put for now. **I WILL NOT LEAVE WITHOUT TOM**. Bride has to keep running out to pass messages to Captain Smith.

40 *Titanic* sent out distress signal: **CQD CQD – "MGY require immediate assistance. Position 41.46 N. 50.14 W."** CQD was the internationally recognised distress signal. SOS was new so both would have been used. Additionally, MGY was the call sign for RMS *Titanic* – this message gives the ships position and calls for immediate assistance.

I hope the Carpathia gets here soon. People are getting frightened outside. I can hear them shouting over the music. I asked Bride about it and he said the band were playing to **CALM THE PASSENGERS**. I'm not sure it's working.

2.10 A.M. [41]

The last lifeboats have gone. The Carpathia is nowhere to be seen. The bow is now completely underwater. It is hard to stand, people are sliding down the deck. It is hard to write. I am going to tuck my mission report under my life jacket now. Tom thinks if we wait until the ship gets lower in the water we might be able to swim to a lifeboat. I hope he's right. I hope you get to read this. I hope I live to give it to you and the Telegraph Team in person. I hope I live to see Mother and Ginny again.

I hope I live.

41 The lights on *Titanic* went out at 2.17 p.m.

Dear Dot,

I really hope you're OK. Last night, Walter came to our door and was banging loud enough to wake the dead. He asked when I had last heard from you and if you really had left on Titanic as planned. I told him you had and showed him the Marconigram you sent.

He said he'd been experimenting with his radio when he heard a distress call from Titanic but I told him that was **IMPOSSIBLE**! What kind of trouble could the 'unsinkable' Titanic possibly be in? But he was sure he'd heard right. We ran to my radio and tuned into the same frequency. I waited, thinking Walter had misheard, or was playing a silly joke. But then we heard it.

CQD – "MGY require immediate assistance. Position 41.46 N. 50.14 W."

My blood ran cold. I left Walter by the radio and ran down the road to wake your dad, hammering on the front door until he opened it, still in his pyjamas. I told him about the distress call, but he thought it was a hoax. I wanted to believe him, but I had a really funny feeling about it ... I made him come and hear it himself.

"CQD CQD SOS de MGY Position 41.44N 50.24W. Require immediate assistance. Come at once. We have struck an iceberg. Sinking."

He still thought it was a hoax, but he thought we should tell the police, just in case. We ran straight to the police station to tell them what we had heard.[42] We had to wake the officer up, and he wasn't pleased.

"You amateurs and your radios! I can't sound the alarm every time you hear a rumour on the airwaves. What do you expect me to do from here? Go home. Everything looks better once the sun is up."

I hope he's right. I wish I could contact you somehow. I know I'm not going to sleep until I know you are okay. I will send this letter with your Dad. He said he was going to travel to the city first thing to find out what's happening. I hope you are all right.

Love,

Dash

TITANIC SUNK
ALL SAVED ABOARD CARPATHIA

TITANIC SINKS
LOSS OF LIFE UNLIKELY DUE TO SHIPS IN VICINITY[43]

42 Sound far-fetched? Perhaps a little, but radio enthusiasts picked up *Titanic*'s distress calls from far away. In South Wales, an engineer named Artie Moore was so worried about what he heard that he reported it to the police. Nobody believed Artie, until the news hit the papers two days later. Marconi was so impressed that he gave Artie a job with the company. In 1932, Artie patented an early version of the sonar system.

43 News regarding the sinking of *Titanic* and who had survived was slow. Rumours spread quickly and some even made it to the front pages of the newspapers.

Date: 17th April 1912

The Marconi International Marine Communication Co., Ltd

Handed in at: CARPATHIA	CHARGES TO PAY.		
	TOTAL		

To: Stephen Baxter

TITANIC SUNK. FAMILY SAFE. PICKED UP BY CARPATHIA. MANY LOST. MEET IN NEW YORK. DON'T WORRY. DOT.

MISSION REPORT – 15TH–18TH APRIL 1912

FROM RMS CARPATHIA

We are safe, and by some miracle so is my mission report. It is a little wet around the edges but the leather wallet Grandma gave me kept it from getting completely ruined. Thanks Grandma!

After I finished writing, Bride came back from speaking to the Captain and told us the last lifeboat was gone. I thought all hope was lost. We stayed in the radio room as we didn't know what else to do.

Phillips stayed at the key messaging for help. He was so determined that he didn't even stop when a man tried to steal the life belt he was wearing. Bride had to bash the thief over the head to stop him.

Not long after, the Captain dismissed the crew. "Men, you have done your full duty. You can do no more. Abandon your cabin. Now it's every man for himself."

I didn't think there was much hope for a couple of kids like Tom and I. Bride remembered seeing a collapsible lifeboat out on deck. He said he thought it had probably gone, but it was worth a shot.

It was there. There was a crowd around it, but they couldn't work out how to set it up. Bride pushed to the front to help, when a colossal wave washed over the deck and dragged the boat and us into the freezing water. The water was so cold it burned. I was gasping with the shock of it. I knew I had to get out as soon as possible or I would be a goner.

My lifebelt kept me afloat but made it hard to swim. I could see the collapsible lifeboat. It wasn't the right way up, but it was afloat. Tom and I swam to it as hard as we could and scrambled aboard.

Others joined us. We were crushed together and there were so many of us I was scared it would sink. Tom and I clung to each other for warmth and for fear that we would be pulled from the boat. I looked around for Bride but I could not see him.

Titanic was almost vertical in the water. She looked beautiful. It sounds strange but she did. So huge, sparks gushing from her funnel. Tom said there must have been some sort of explosion in the engine room. I watched to keep my eyes off what was happening in the water. There were people in lifebelts as far as the eye could see, desperate for help. When the ship was gone, that's all there was left. Cries for help. We did what we could and pulled a man on board. He was shaking with cold and so pale in the moonlight that it took a moment to recognize him. It was Bride! I wanted to help others, but there were so many. We were scared the boat might sink. I thought of the first lifeboats that left half-filled when ours was the wrong way up and full to bursting. Someone suggested we say a prayer. There was nothing else we could do.

Eventually the cries for help faded to something worse. Silence. The cold had overcome all of the brave souls that had managed to escape the sinking Titanic, only to perish in the water. I felt lonely in our tiny boat in the huge ocean. The stars twinkled above our heads and I wondered if we would ever be found. One of the right-way-up lifeboats came towards us looking for survivors. Finding none in the water, they took us aboard.

I clung to Tom and waited. I remembered dear Meg. Thank goodness we had left her with Grandma. With so little room in the lifeboats, I would never have been able to save her. I was glad she was safe, even if I might never see her again.[44] I must have slept a little because the next thing I remember it was dawn. Someone on board the lifeboat said they could see a ship. Tom and I were taken aboard in a net, hauled up the side of the ship like fish.

As I looked down at the lifeboat I could see a man lying in the bottom. I couldn't see his face but I just knew he hadn't survived. I was so sad. He had been so close to being saved.

44 Only 3 of the 12 dogs on board *Titanic* survived.

Some brave souls climbed up a rope ladder. One of them was Bride. I don't know how he managed it. He collapsed when he got to the top and was taken to the ship's hospital.

On board, I was given something warm to drink. It felt good in my hands but it **BURNED MY THROAT**.[45] It was nice to get rid of the salty taste, though.

Tom spotted Mother and Ginny and we ran to them. Mother almost collapsed with relief, she hugged us so tightly, I worried she might not let us go. Ginny asked me if I had brought her a fairing biscuit. She was so confused. Lots of people kept coming over to ask us if we had seen their husband or son or friend, trying to work out where their loved ones were. It was so sad.

The passengers on the Carpathia couldn't be nicer. They were on their way to Europe but they still turned and came to our aid as soon as they heard the distress signal. They have leant us fresh clothes because ours were all wet and stiff with salt. I am wearing an itchy wool dress that is far too big for me. But it is warm. Mother fussed about getting our coats dry so we could put them back on. Mothers can be **SO ODD** some times.

I went to find Bride in the ship's hospital, but I was told he was in the Marconi Room on the Carpathia. I couldn't believe he was **STILL WORKING** after everything. He couldn't talk long as he

---

45 Passengers brought aboard the *Carpathia* were given brandy to help warm them up and treat them for shock. Something not done today.

was helping Carpathia's radio operator send messages to let the survivors' families know they were safe. I asked him if he had seen Phillips. He went pale. Phillips had been in our boat but had died. I knew then it was Phillips who I had seen as we were hauled up the side. I'm sure I will never meet braver men than Bride and Phillips. Phillips to have stayed at the key so long and Bride to be back at the key so soon. They are as brave as Jack Binns.

I scribbled a quick message to you and Father. Bride said he'd send it. I hope you get it, otherwise you might think we're still safely aboard Titanic. Or you might have heard about the disaster and think the worst! I don't want you to worry. We'll be with you soon.

Mother, Ginny and I are sharing a cabin with a lovely family who have been so helpful. Tom is sleeping in the library with the few other men and boys that made it off the boat.[46] There are people sleeping under tables, in bathtubs, in the corridors. I spoke to Eva Hart whose mother who had been too frightened to put on her night clothes aboard Titanic. She said they were sleeping on deck. They are too frightened to sleep inside the ship, in case Carpathia was to sink too! Her father is not with them. She said she is hoping that he has been picked up by another ship. I hope she is right.[47]

I saw Mrs Laroche, with her girls. I was so relieved to see them safe. She said her husband had put them in a lifeboat before Titanic sank. He is not on board Carpathia. She hopes he has been picked up by another ship, but fears the worst.

---

46 Lifeboats were loaded with women and children first. 80% of the men who boarded *Titanic* died in the disaster.
47 There were lots of rumours about other rescue vessels and where the survivors were being taken. The *Carpathia* was the only ship to find survivors at the scene.

I feel lucky to be alive and lucky to know you and Father are safely in New York. So many people have lost loved ones. It's heart-breaking.

Some of the ladies from first class are trying to arrange help for people who have lost everything. They came over to ask me what our situation was like and I said I was worried because "**ALL OUR WORLDLY GOODS**" had been lost. They were kind and asked Mother to come and speak to them when Ginny woke up from her nap. But Mother said we had lost very little compared to some people. We had each other and that was more than many could boast.

I offered to help in any way I could and they asked me to take a message to the Marconi room for them. It was an order for clothes from the department stores they owned for the survivors.

It won't be long until we arrive.

I hope you got our message. I can't imagine how worried you must be.

Dot

Dear Dash,

We arrived in New York just before 10 o'clock last night.
I am sure our arrival must have been very different to
yours. Word of the sinking of Titanic has spread and the
port was filled with anxious relatives and members of the
press wanting to hear our stories. We were whisked off
the boat. We didn't have to go through the usual customs
checks because almost none of Titanic's passengers had any
of their papers with them.

Many people had lost everything. I asked Mother what
we would do without all our belongings. We needed the
money from the sale of the house to get the apple farm
up and running! But she said not to worry. Belongings were
replaceable and we still had the **COATS ON OUR BACKS**.
She gave me a wink and tapped her nose. Very odd!

Father met us at Pier 54 and I was so pleased to see him.
He said the news of what had happened to Titanic and who
had survived was so mixed up that he didn't dare hope we
were safe until we were in his arms.

Back at the hotel, Mother took out a little pair of
pocket scissors and unpicked a seam in my coat. Then she

pulled out a **GOLD COIN**! She had sewn some money in each of our coats![48] There was a small fortune, and though we had lost a lot when the boat sank, there was still some money in the bank in England, so it was going to be all right. We could buy anything else we needed in New York.

I have the **MISSION REPORT** you asked for, but I don't have the radio kit Grandad put together for me. I feel silly feeling sad about that, when so many have lost **EVERYTHING**. And so many more have lost their lives.

We will stay in the city for a few more days and then Father says we'll come to the orchard and put all this behind us. As much as I want to, I don't think I will ever be able to put what happened on board Titanic behind me. To think all of those **PEOPLE** who will **NEVER COME HOME**! And that grand ship, at the bottom of the ocean. Think of all the work people like your Uncle Michael put into it. The people that lost their lives building it. The staircase, the Marconi room, the swimming pool, the vast engines and the electric camel now all lie somewhere at the bottom of the freezing ocean, never to be seen again.

How can I put that behind me? How can anyone?

See you soon,

Dot

---

48 Many passengers were travelling to America to start a new life. To keep their money safe, they hid it in their clothes.

DOT CAN YOU HEAR ME? IS IT WORKING?

DOT ARE YOU THERE?

YES! I'M HERE! IT'S WORKING.

GREAT. I WAS WORRIED HARRY
HADN'T SET IT UP RIGHT.

HE HADN'T BUT I FIXED IT.
I TOLD HIM WE'D SEE HIM AND
THE TELEGRAPH TEAM TOMORROW
FOR MY FIRST MISSION.

IT'S YOUR SECOND.
YOUR FIRST WAS THE MOST
DANGEROUS OF ALL TIME.

I KNOW.
MOTHER SAYS HURRY UP AND
COME OVER FOR DINNER.

AS SOON AS I'M OFF THE
RADIO.

COME ON THEN.

DOT?

WHAT?

I'M GLAD YOU ARE HERE.
I'M GLAD YOU ARE SAFE.

ME TOO.
DON'T BE SOPPY.

EPILOGUE

Dear Dotty,

I don't suppose anyone calls you Dotty anymore do they? Ha! You will always be Dotty to me. Besides, there isn't much you can do about it in a letter, so Dotty it is.

Seems a bit old fashioned to be writing a letter but it seemed more fitting than picking up the phone considering the news. We were such letter-writers back in the day. Could you imagine if they had phones back then? We would never have been off them I'm sure. Think of the bills we would have racked up. My son Andrew has a 'mobile phone'[49] if you can believe it. Works on radio waves just like our old sets. A bit more advanced of course. I tried to tell him I had the idea first. Do you remember? You'll have to back me up the next time we come to the farm.

Did you see on the news that they have found Titanic? A team of explorers found it with their undersea robots.

49 The first mobile phone call was made on 3rd April 1973. The first mobile phone you could buy, the Motorola DynaTAC, was released 1983. It was VERY expensive, costing around $4000.

WRECKAGE OF TITANIC DISCOVERED

An American and French team have found the wreck of the famous luxury liner, sunk on its maiden voyage 12,000 ft beneath the surface of the Atlantic Ocean. The team leader, Dr Robert Ballard said,

"Our initial reaction was excitement, then a coming down off that to realize we had found the ship where 1,500 people had died."

It is incredible to think that she has been lying there at the bottom of the ocean for all these years. I wonder what secrets she still holds.

I was wondering how you felt about it. You didn't speak much about the disaster when you got back, but I am sure you must have thought about it often. I dug out your old mission report. Shall I bring it up to the farm next time I come over? We could get the Telegraph Team together. Is Alex still down the road?

Love,

Dash

Dear Dash,

How lovely to receive a letter, and yes, how old fashioned. I'll have you know some people do call me Dotty, not many, but I always think of you when they do.

I did see the news of the Ballard expedition. It brought it all flooding back. I haven't spoken of Titanic in a long time. After we arrived in New York on the Carpathia, Mother and Father said we were starting a new life and that we were lucky to be able to do so when so many others weren't. We all shared what had happened with Father and that was that. At night I would think about it - and about you that night. Standing next to your radio, hearing the distress call with Walter. Goodness, you were quite the engineer weren't you?

Now everyone wants to talk about Titanic. I've been called by reporters who to want to interview me about what happened. I was only a child, but the few child survivors are the only people still around who are able to describe first-hand what happened.

It still hurts to think about it, after all this time, but I want to tell people about what happened on board the ship, about all those interesting people I met that lost their lives and about the brave men in the Marconi Room. I'm glad you still have my mission report. I'd love to see it. In fact, I have a few pages to add to it. I didn't think it was quite complete. I'll show you when you come over.

I have another present for you, too. One you have been waiting a long time for.

Do you still hear from any of the Telegraph Team? We did have some adventures together, didn't we? Alex is still down the road, it was her who phoned and told me to switch on the TV to see the news about Titanic.

And yes, I can believe your son has a mobile phone, if he's anything like his dad, I'm sure he was first in line. I'm only surprised he didn't build it himself. Perhaps you could use it to give me a call! It will be much easier than writing letters or tapping it out in code. Though I suppose it is a little less fun.

Love,
Dot

P.S. Do bring Andrew's mobile phone. I'd love to take a look!

MISSION REPORT — AFTER THE VOYAGE

The Titanic and 1,517 of the passengers she carried never completed the voyage. I met so many wonderful people on board, I didn't feel my mission would be complete until I found out what happened to them. I followed all the articles in the newpapers which were filled with stories of survivors and news of the trial that followed for months after the disaster.

PASSENGER UPDATES

CAPTAIN EDWARD JOHN SMITH
After finding out the ship was sinking, he ordered the uncovering, loading and lowering of the lifeboats but made no attempt to save himself.

Some believe Captain Smith contributed to the sinking of the Titanic by not slowing down after warnings of ice in the region. The last time I saw Captain Smith, he was on Titanic's bridge after dismissing the crew.

EVA & ESTHER HART
Eva and her mother escaped Titanic on lifeboat 14 and were taken aboard the Carpathia. Eva's father, Benjamin wrapped her in a blanket before saying goodbye. Sadly, Eva's father did not survive.

VICTOR GAITAN ANDREA GIGLIO & BENJAMIN GUGGENHEIM

According to reports Victor and Mr Guggenheim dressed in their evening clothes and helped women and children into lifeboats. According to one survivor Guggenheim said, "We have dressed up in our best and are prepared to go down like gentlemen."

After the sinking, I read that Victor's former headteacher said of him, "Those who knew Giglio at school will not require any assurance that he met death bravely and even willingly rather than, perhaps, take the place of someone else in the lifeboats."

Neither Victor nor Mr Guggenheim survived.

THE LAROCHE FAMILY

I was relieved to see Mrs Laroche and her daughters aboard the Carpathia, but Mr Laroche was not so lucky. He is believed to have gone down with the ship. The Laroche family returned to France instead of travelling on to Haiti.

JACK PHILLIPS

Jack Phillips died in a lifeboat shortly before dawn on 15th April. His heroism aboard RMS Titanic was commemorated by an 80 ft sq cloister built in a park in his home town of Godalming in Surrey. Inside the cloister stands a stone tablet remembering Jack Phillips, paid for by the Marconi Company.

HAROLD BRIDE

After spending some time in the hospital aboard the Carpathia, Bride worked in the radio room with Harold Cottam, sending out countless messages from passengers. After arriving in New York, Bride gave his story to the New York Times. I'm not sure what happened to him after that, but I believe he moved to Scotland to work in sales.

JOSEPH BRUCE ISMAY

Mr Ismay escaped Titanic in collapsible lifeboat C. I did not see him aboard the Carpathia. Apparently he had demanded a private cabin and barely left it. I heard a lot about him after the sinking. Many believed, that as a White Star employee, a person responsible for the number of lifeboats on board, he should not have taken a place in one but should have gone down with the ship like Captain Smith. There were all kinds of stories, from him having left in the first lifeboat, to him being rowed away from the ship by his own crew. I know a lot of people were angry with him.

After arriving in New York, I read that he was called as a witness at the trial, where he claimed he had every right to save his own life as he was just a passenger and not a member of the crew. The newspapers said terrible things about him. After the trial, Ismay returned to England, his reputation in tatters. From what I read it seems he never recovered from the shock of the disaster.

MR JOHN PRIEST

Mr Priest managed to swim to lifeboat 15. As he was wearing only shorts and a vest, he suffered frostbite. His survival was miraculous considering how deep he was within the ship when Titanic collided with the iceberg. Even more miraculously, Mr Priest survived **THREE** further sinkings during his career including the sinking of Titanic's sister ship the Brittanic after she struck a mine 1916 during the First World War.

MR CHARLES GOODWIN

Neither Charles, his mother and father nor any of his five siblings survived the sinking of RMS Titanic. Out of a total of 709 third-class passengers aboard Titanic only 172 survived. In the inquiry that followed, some spoke of how the third-class passengers' way to the boat deck was blocked by gates as stewards waited for instructions to open them. Due to where third-class passengers were on the ship at the time of the disaster, it would have been harder for them to make it to the boat deck before the lifeboats were launched.

SECRET RECIPE

Grandma's Fairings

You will need:
100 g butter, cold
225 g plain flour
2 tsp baking powder
1 ½ tsp baking soda
1 tsp mixed spice
1 tsp cinnamon
2 tsp ground ginger
100 g caster sugar
4 tbsp golden syrup
2 tsp lemon zest

1. Ask an adult to preheat the oven to 180 °C / gas mark 4. Take a baking sheet and cut a piece of greaseproof paper large enough to cover it.

2. Tip the flour, baking powder, baking soda, spices into a large bowl and mix together well.

3. Add the butter and use your fingertips to rub it into the flour until there are no large lumps of butter and your bowl looks like it is full of little crumbs. Add the zest and the sugar and stir well.

4. Add the syrup and mix together with your hands until you have a soft dough.

5. Use a tablespoon to take lumps of dough and roll them into balls the size of ping-pong balls and put them on the tray 5 cm apart.

6. Ask an adult to put the tray into the oven for 10 minutes until golden.

7. Leave to cool.

TRUE OR FALSE?

False

Dorothy (Dot), William (Dash) and their families didn't really exist, but families like theirs certainly did. Albert, the kind steward that showed Dorothy and Tom around *Titanic*, was made up, too. The Telegraph Team didn't exist either, but children like them did. Books about electronics and wireless telegraphy were very popular at the turn of the century. Amateurs, young and old, built their own sets to experiment with this exciting new technology, communicate with one another and to arrange adventures just like the ones William describes. The Telegraph Team are based on characters from a series of books that was popular in the 1920s. The series was called *The Radio Boys* and each book had an introduction written by the heroic Marconi Operator Jack Binns himself!

True

RMS *Titanic* did set sail on 10th April, 1912. It really did strike an iceberg on 14th April and *Titanic* really did sink in the early hours of the 15th April. All of the passengers and crew in Dorothy's mission report are real. Eva and Esther Hart, the Goodwins, the Laroches, Captain Smith, Jack Phillips, Harold Bride, John Priest, Mr Ismay, Benjamin Guggenheim and Victor Giglio and their stories are based on the accounts of survivors of the disaster.

THE SINKING OF RMS *TITANIC*

In the early hours of the morning of 15th April 1912, RMS *Titanic* sank beneath the icy waters of the Atlantic Ocean just four days into its first voyage. Of the 2,229 people on board only 713 survived, 498 passengers and 215 crew.

After *Titanic* sank, inquiries into the disaster took place on both sides of the Atlantic. No blame was laid at the feet of any of the surviving passengers or crew or even the White Star Line. However, the inquiries did decide the following:

- *Ships must carry enough lifeboats to accommodate all passengers and crew on board.*
- *Radios on board ships must be manned 24 hours a day.*

It is believed a ship named *Californian* was only 19 miles away from *Titanic* at the time of the sinking but its crew was unaware of the accident due to the radio operator having signed off for the night.

Was *Titanic* travelling too fast?

Many believe Captain Smith was under pressure to make the crossing in as short a time as possible in order for *Titanic* to be named the fastest and most magnificent ship. They believe that travelling at such speed after receiving warnings of ice in the area was dangerous and that Captain Smith should have ordered the crew to slow down. Many believe one of the people responsible for the pressure on Captain Smith was Joseph Bruce Ismay.

Bad News for the Telegraph Team

As soon as the first telegraphs about the disaster were received by the Marconi station in Newfoundland, Canada, people hit the telegraphs clamouring for news which jammed up the airwaves. This made it hard for information to get through and led to newspapers printing stories based on false information. Ships at sea at the time reported interference from amateur operators on land. There was a lot of confusion and many claimed amateur radio users were partly to blame.

Three months after the disaster, the United States Congress passed the *Radio Act of 1912*, which limited the range of amateur radio sets. The act, which became law in August of the same year required all amateur radio enthusiasts to have a licence and required all radio users to give right of way to distress signals from ships or face heavy fines.

The Discovery of RMS *Titanic*

RMS *Titanic* fascinated people from the moment it left the dock in Belfast. After it sank, this fascination grew. People wanted to know everything about what happened to *Titanic*, how the ship sank and what secrets it took to the bottom of the Atlantic. Teams from around the world searched for the wreck and came up with all kinds of ways to raise *Titanic* from the ocean floor, but no one knew exactly where she was.

On 1st September 1985, Dr Robert Ballard and his team did what no one else had managed. Their submersible camera named the Argo, developed for secret military operations, sent footage of one of *Titanic*'s boilers up from the sea floor. It was the first time anyone had seen *Titanic* in more than 70 years. The film and pictures they took showed not only the boiler but the crow's nest, the Grand Staircase, the bow, as well as dinner plates and a case of champagne.

Titanic today

Since the discovery of the wreck, thousands of items have been recovered. Everything from door knobs and dinner plates to jewellery and watches belonging to people on board.

If you have a lot of money, you can even visit the *Titanic*. A tour company will take you to explore the *Titanic* wreck site for over $105,000. This is about as much as a first class ticket aboard *Titanic* would be today. However, if you want to see *Titanic*, you will have to go soon. Scientists believe that bacteria able to live in extreme conditions will consume the wreck within the next 15 or 20 years.

TIMELINE OF THE *TITANIC*

29th July 1908

Plans for RMS *Titanic* are approved by the White Star Line.

31st March 1909

Work building RMS *Titanic* begins at the Harland and Wolff shipyard in Belfast.

20th October 1910

RMS *Olympic* is launched from Harland and Wolff Shipyard.

31st May 1911

Midday – Hull of RMS *Titanic* is launched from Harland and Wolff shipyard, Belfast.

2nd April 1912

Fully completed RMS *Titanic* leaves Belfast bound for Southampton for its maiden voyage.

4th April 1912

RMS *Titanic* arrives in Southampton.

10th April 1912

Midday – RMS *Titanic* sets sail on its maiden voyage from Southampton, England.

10th April 1912 - 6.30 p.m.

RMS *Titanic* arrives in Cherbourg, France to pick up passengers.

11th April - 11.30 a.m.

RMS *Titanic* arrives in Queenstown (now Cobh), Ireland.

14th April - multiple times

RMS *Titanic* receives warnings regarding icebergs throughout the day.

14th April - 11.40 p.m.

Lookout alerts Captain Smith to iceberg in RMS *Titanic*'s path. RMS *Titanic* strikes iceberg damaging its starboard bow. Water begins to enter the ship.

15th April - Midnight

Captain Smith goes below deck with ship's designer Thomas Andrews and discovers two watertight compartments filled with water and four more filling rapidly. RMS *Titanic* will sink in a couple of hours.

15th April - 12.05 a.m.

Captain Smith orders crew to uncover the lifeboats.

15th April - 12.15 a.m.

Captain Smith orders Harold Bride and Jack Phillips to send emergency messages to ships in the area.

15th April - 12.45 a.m.

First lifeboat is lowered with only 27 people aboard despite the lifeboats being designed to hold 65. RMS *Carpathia* receives RMS *Titanic*'s distress call from 58 miles away.

15th April - 2.05 a.m.

Last two lifeboats lowered.

15th April - 2.17 a.m.

RMS *Titanic*'s bow is submerged. Captain Smith dismisses his crew announcing every man for himself. The band stops playing.

15th April - 2.20 a.m.

RMS *Titanic* disappears from view as it sinks to the bottom of the Atlantic Ocean just 2 hours and 40 minutes after striking the iceberg.

15th April - 4.10 a.m.

RMS *Carpathia* picks up first lifeboat.

15th April - 8.30 a.m.

Last lifeboat containing survivors recovered.

15th April - 8.50 a.m.

RMS *Carpathia* leaves the area with just 705 survivors aboard.

17th April

RMS *Titanic* was due to arrive in New York on Wednesday morning.

18th April - 9.00 p.m.

RMS *Carpathia* arrives in New York.

22nd April - 15th May

Ships sent to site of RMS *Titanic*'s sinking recover 328 bodies from the water.

19th April - 25th May

Enquiry into the disaster is held by the United States Senate.

2nd May - 3rd July

Enquiry into the disaster by the British.

1st September, 1985

Expedition lead by Robert Ballard discovers the wreck of RMS *Titanic*.

31st May, 2009

The last survivor or the sinking of RMS *Titanic*, Eliza Gladys Dean, who was two months old at the time of the disaster, dies aged 97.

If you enjoyed *My Best Friend on the Titanic*, why not read:

My
Best Friend

THE EVACUEE

Sally
Morgan

Illustrated by
Gareth
Conway